Epicaricacy

Short Stories of Christopher Boden

ISBN: 978-1-7375680-2-5

First Edition

Printed and bound in the USA

First printing November 2021

Editing and Book Design by: Casey Rose

Cover Design by: Emily Lynn

DEDICATION

The only thing that you can forever rely upon is change.
As we move through our own private universe the
individual stars of friends, lovers, and family will all change
and evolve. Often appearing out of the void at random
times, and yet always when you needed to find them. Some
will just glance by at the edges, some crashing through like
a comet, and some burning brightly for eons. Always
changing, always evolving, always enduring.

For all of those that have passed through the lopsided
galaxy that is my life, who have given me the honor of
feeling your light upon my face, to all of you who have
helped shape the man I am today, and given me such
wonderful stories to share...

This is for you.

The most valuable gift you are ever given is Time. The
only thing you get to keep, if you're lucky, are memories.
At the end of it all, those are all that really matters.

Scribed within are some of my good memories, enjoy
them, share them, and maybe even learn a few things along
the way.

Thank you for sharing your time with me. I appreciate you
more than you will ever imagine.

- cb

TABLE OF CONTENTS

DISCLAIMER

These works, and everyone contained within, are works of creative fiction from the mind of Chris Boden, who is himself a figment of your imagination. Any resemblance to people or places you may be familiar with, real or imagined, is purely coincidental and most likely caused by a small programming glitch in the simulation within which you exist.

Don't even fucking think about suing me, or I shall visit you in the small hours and leave your refrigerator door open just enough that the light doesn't come on after sprinkling your carpet with Legos. If people mentioned in this work of fiction cause you grief or concern, perhaps it's time to make some new life choices and stop being such a cunt, eh?

1

THE PEANUT BUTTER STORY

Size matters, and I'm a skinny little shit.

Despite the fact that I have the wingspan of an Albatross, I have the waist of a Dachshund. I've always been the skinny guy. As a result of that, I've been the go-to person to be crammed into places other people wouldn't fit for my entire life.

There's a tiny locomotive currently sitting in Coopersville - a diminutive, US Army, 20-ton Whitcomb that looks more like a toy train than a real one. If you ever wondered what it would be like if you cross-bred a Smart Car with a Diesel Locomotive, this is it. Decades ago, when I was a twelve-year-old boy, it was owned by the Muskegon Hysterical Society. One summer afternoon, when all the king's coffee and all the king's men couldn't put Whitcomb together again, I was voluntold to wedge my skinny ass in there to help change out the carbon brushes on the motor.

Railroad men don't tend to run on the small side. Stumpy, sure, but even the "little" guys on a railroad tend to have thighs like tree trunks. They all crowded around the side of that little tan engine and watched me disappear inside through a tiny opening. I would reach out my hand with a set of brushes in it. Some nice gentlemen that I couldn't see, would take them and hand over a shiny new set. Then my hand would vanish back into the darkness of the engine bay. This process repeated and after a while a scrawny little fucker, covered in schmoo, emerged triumphant from the little door.

The amount of times I've been the one to go into places other people either can't fit or won't go is off the fucking charts. Tight, deep, high, cold, dangerous, or inaccessible has been a recurring theme in my life for as long as I can remember. The odd thing is that I enjoy it - most of the time. There are certainly exceptions, though. When you spend a lot of time doing either confined space or high-altitude work, you're going to occasionally have at least a few unpleasant experiences.

I've encountered a grease tank the size of a small swimming pool in the basement of an abandoned smoked sausage factory that would not just give you nightmares, it would fuck you up for years. I'll skip painting a vivid mental picture and simply say, I've never seen so many flies.

I've traversed a train bridge across the Grand River to explore a gigantic steel gear (it was a swing bridge in a former life) and seen a span the length of a football field that was completely covered in large, very well-fed spiders.

I once dropped into a utility vault and was all the way to the floor before we realized that we'd just come down a ladder that was two feet away from a wasp nest the size of a basketball. That was a bit scary, the terrifying part is that we were now inside a ten-foot concrete cube and the only way out was back up that ladder. You couldn't have got a pin up my ass with a jackhammer, and that is the day I learned how to run up a ladder.

But all those stories can wait for another day because nothing, fucking nothing, compares to the peanut butter jacuzzi.

So, here is the story of why I can't eat peanut butter.

For almost every school day of my entire misspent youth, we walked across the parking lot of the big, tan building on the corner of our neighborhood. It was the shortcut to the railroad tracks we hiked on our way to and from school. Never did we bother to learn what they made inside the factory, but once in a while we'd ride our bikes through the big pile of sawdust outside.

When I was 19, my dad's company was hired to design and build a machine for them, and I got my first look at what they actually produced there.

Bird feeders – specifically, suet cakes - and tons of them! Little blocks of suet or peanut butter, mixed with bird seed, that people put in backyard feeders for wild birds. Dad's job was to build a machine that would prepare the peanut butter for the assembly line.

It was a complicated machine with some interesting components; it looked like a large box about the size of five cubic feet. There was a small hatch on top, about eight-by-twelve inches. It had a small ramp that sloped down to the hatch and was about two feet long. The ramp is where the operator would place a fifty-pound block of peanut butter. At that stage, the peanut butter was very similar to the stuff you'd find in a peanut butter cup, firm and almost crumbly.

The operator would place these peanut butter blocks on the ramp, slide them through the hatch, and then they would fall into the box. The only other openings to the box were where a driveshaft for the big mixing auger passed through right in the middle of the top, and a small hole about an inch in diameter on the bottom where the pipe was welded in place for the output.

Inside the box was a giant "mixing paddle" - it was actually made from a snowblower auger. It was cheaper to buy a brand new one than to fabricate the part from scratch. The auger was the size you'd find in a garden-tractor-style snowblower. It stood on end, with a block of UHMW (Ultra High Molecular Weight) polyethylene as a bearing on the top and bottom, and a driveshaft from a motor coming down from the top of the box.

Everything was designed to be hosed down and cleaned, and the auger moved slowly on its axis, so just making the shaft end smooth and letting it ride in a hole in a block of UHMW worked perfectly. For applications like this, it's the "poor man's Teflon" and works great when you need something to slide against something else while being wet or food-safe because it will never rust.

The outside of the tank was wrapped in a beautiful and intricate zigzag of copper pipe that went up and down all the way around the entire box. Hot water was pumped through the pipes to heat the entire tank and melt the peanut butter until it had the consistency of bearing grease so that it could be pumped down the line. The pipes were wrapped in an outer box shell and the space between the inner box and outer shell was filled with insulation.

The whole point was to load in about 1500 pounds of peanut butter, heat it until it melted into goop, mix it well, and send it down the pipe to be mixed with birdseed and then pooped out in little dollops into its packaging. It had to be melted, otherwise it was too thick to pump. Even the output pipe had to be wrapped with a heated water jacket or the peanut butter would solidify in the pipe and clog everything. Peanut butter is a pain in the ass to work with.

It was my job to wire up the machine that dad had built. There wasn't much to it, and I was thrilled at the chance to do such a serious and important job for dad. I'd never wired up someone else's project before, so even for something so simple, I was honored.

It wasn't exactly rocket surgery, but I was an idiot apprentice at the time. The whole setup was run off a couple of relays and thermostats. The machine was made to be set-and-forget. A motor for the output pump, a motor for the mixer, the pump and valve for the hot water… that was it - easy. No PLCs or anything fancy, just a thermostat, a couple of motors, and a handful of relays in a little control box. It was as simple as it could be, and that was the point. It didn't need to be fancy, it needed to be reliable.

I spent a whole weekend doing all of the wiring. I had a pretty solid idea of what I was doing, but I'd never worked with anything at this scale before. I didn't even draw a schematic. It was simple, and I just kept it all in my head as I went. The first time I turned it on, one of the little Omron relays did a convincing impersonation of a grenade. A small mistake, but an expensive one. Dad got me a new relay after I changed a few backward connections, and it came to life.

I was ecstatic. I ran and got dad and showed him my handiwork. I was standing there beaming at the magnificent contraption that I had brought to life. There really wasn't anything to see, but the lights came on, the motor hummed, and the relays clicked. I was beaming with pride at my accomplishment.

Dad gave it a thorough check to see that everything was working just so and asked me to hand him a screwdriver and a pair of dikes (diagonal wire cutters). I pulled them off the bench and watched him open up the control box, which puffed out with a massive wad of orange wires when he opened the door. The wad of wires floofed out like an afro to be proud of and was easily double the size of the small enclosure from where it emerged.

Dad sighed, and simply said, "Orange?"

Orange was the first spool of wire I'd grabbed… and the only one. It was simply the closest spool on the shelf, the right size, and had enough to do the whole job.

I stood there thinking about how it was going to take me a full five minutes to pack all that shit back in there as dad calmly unplugged the machine, walked back over to the control box, and proceeded to give it a boot-camp haircut.

I didn't know whether to shit or go blind.

"What the fuck, dad? That took me two days! It worked! How the fuck am I supposed to know how to hook all that back up? I had a system!"

"It looks like the drippings from a drunken fuck," he said, "There's no way we hand off work like that to a client. What you made was a prototype, now make it pretty. If YOU can't tell how the wires go together then sure as hell no one else can either. Someone will have to fix this someday. You owe it to them, the client, and me to make this not only work but able to be fixed easily when it doesn't. The guy who fixes this ten years from now might be you. Now do it right."

And that was my lesson in craftsmanship. It was a lesson cemented into my brain over the many hours I spent meditating upon the thoughts like, "I've quit better jobs than this," and doing a mental feasibility study on leaving a few slices of ham tucked deep in the cabin air vents of his truck.

There's a lot of guys who talk about craftsmanship and never really bother to explain exactly what that is. Craftsmanship is the hours of work you put in when the job is done and the damn thing works fine, to make it not only work well but make it pretty. It's a mixture of engineering and art.

Every young engineering student is taught that "Form Follows Function". Craftsmanship is learning that "Form" can have an artistic aspect as well, and that "Function" can mean allowing it to be easier to repair, easier to clean, etc. It's not just taking into account the machine as it is today, but as it will be in the future decades to come.

Most people don't think of skilled labor as a form of artistic expression, but ask any electrician, plumber, framer, or welder, and they will all tell you that craftsmanship is absolutely an artform. It's just a form of art that only those that work in the field ever appreciate, to the rest of the world it's invisible.

Any electrician worth a damn can open a box and tell you the skill level of the original builder. They judge each other on such things constantly. It's nuanced, subtle, and intricate. Every one of the trades does this in some way, and there's just as much time, effort, and genius that goes into running conduit as there is for carving a marble sculpture or composing a symphony. We live in a world where the majority of our art is functional, invisible, and only appreciated by a silent army of people who are reluctant to share their secrets.

I spent another two days rewiring the machine, with proper color codes and wire routing. I spitefully used an entire bag of dad's good, expensive zip ties on the project. It was art.

I passed the subsequent inspection with flying colors and won the pride of my dad.

Worth it.

A couple of days later, we fumblefucked the machine on a truck and hauled it off to the factory to be installed. The millwrights did their thing and hoisted it up onto the second-floor mezzanine to be bolted in place. The plumbers did their thing and got the water heater hooked up. The electricians did their part and gave us a one-armed-bandit with 20 Amps of 3-phase 480. I'd done my part and was just there as a spectator. Like anyone else, I love hard work - I can watch it all day.

I sat on a pallet and ate several handfuls of gigantic raisins that were originally destined as bird feed. They were fuckin massive, tasted amazing, and went well with the show. I couldn't believe that raisins this big were used as bird feed. They were nothing like the ones you get in the little packs for lunch. I don't know the story on why or whatnot, but I've never had raisins like this anywhere else in my entire life.

By the end of the day, the machine was completely installed, and everything was ready to test. All of the assorted teams were standing around with a thumb up their ass, smoking cigarettes and eating raisins, and it was time to see if all our work was successful in real-world conditions.

Dad stood with the client and gave me the go-ahead. I proudly pushed the green button that started everything up on our machine. It hummed to life and everyone was pleased. Dad spent a couple of minutes kibitzing with the shop manager and letting the machine warm up a bit. Then they told the guys to start loading the tank with blocks of peanut butter.

We all watched as the guys loaded the first thirty blocks into the tank. Thirty blocks doesn't sound like much until you realize, that's three-quarters of a ton of peanut butter!

For several minutes, one at a time, we watched them open the box, pull out the bag, open the bag, set it on the ramp, and slide the block through the hatch. The few to land inside made a bang so loud I thought it might dent the tank, but after half a dozen it was just a mild WHUMP.

It was cool watching something so mission-specific come to life because we didn't know exactly what to expect. This was an original and unique machine, so nobody knew just what it would sound like. Nobody knew its temperaments or personality yet. I was fascinated.

And then, it made a sound.

A bad sound.

An expensive sound.

WHUMPUMPshhhhhhhhWHUMPUMPshhhhhhhhhWH

UMPUMPshhhhhhh

Three people all moved at once to slam the EMERGENCY OFF switch.

There wasn't any way to see inside the tank from the control panel. I knew the mixer was working because the motor on top was spinning, but there wasn't anything on the outside of the box to actually see. The shafts and gearbox were all washdown rated and enclosed.

It took about two minutes for us to figure out just what the hell was wrong. Dad grabbed a flashlight and looked through the hatch and saw that the auger was all cattywampus with the top end hanging from the Lovejoy at a painful angle, and the bottom fucked off into a corner of the little square at the bottom of the tank about 4 inches from where it wanted to be.

As he explained this, I turned as red as the emergency button they had pushed moments before.

I had wired the mixer motor for the giant snowblower auger in such a way that it was spinning in the wrong direction. Instead of pulling the contents at the center of the tank upward, it was pushing the contents down and the tank top had just enough give that when a rather solid chunk of peanut butter got wedged in between the auger and the bottom of the tank, it climbed up out of its lower bearing block and started flopping around inside the tank.

The whole thing only moved at about one revolution per second, but it moved with authority and was chunking around against the inside of a big metal tank. Needless to say, it made a sound...

It was a trivial thing to fix. To change the direction of any three-phase motor all you have to do is disconnect any two of the three power feed wires and reverse them. It took me less than a minute with a screwdriver to get the motor turning in the proper direction.

The problem was that someone still had to get the end of the auger shaft seated back in its bearing block, and that was inside the bottom of the tank...

Which was only accessible through the tiny hatch where the peanut butter goes in...

Which was now heated to a hundred degrees Fahrenheit...

Nobody said a word, nobody ever ordered me in there - they didn't have to. There was a ten-second meeting without a single word being said and where everyone gave me "that look". It was clear that I had been voluntold.

They turned off the heat and I propped open the hatch with a piece of 2x4 that was sitting on the floor. One of the millwrights got a blower with a long yellow tube about 6 inches in diameter and stuffed it through the hatch to blow fresh air inside.

I stripped off my shirt, emptied my pockets, and started towards the tank when dad cleared this throat.

"Um, Son, are you planning on walking home tonight?"

"Uhhhhhhh... no? Why?"

"Because if you wear those pants in there you're not fuckin' sitting in my truck."

"Oh, shit...yeah......... um... I have a problem..."

"What's that?"

"I'm… uh… I'm not wearing any underwear."

The millwrights, the electricians, the plumbers, the client, the shop guys, and no small compliment of the line workers all got a laugh out of that one.

"You ain't got nothing we all haven't seen before, figure it out."

I painfully regretted the fact that I hadn't worn underwear since I was in elementary school, but luckily, I didn't have much time to think about it. I stripped buck naked but put my shoes back on for protection and slipped feet-first through the hatch into the peanut butter hot tub. A pair of guys manned the hatch with the blower and held several flashlights looking inside so that I could see, and so they could keep an eye on me and make sure I didn't die.

It was… disgusting. The goopy mess was everywhere, instantly. At this point in my life, I had long hair that hung in a ponytail halfway to my ass. The tank was over half full and I had to face upwards, reaching behind me to keep my face above the surface and still get the shaft in the hole. It took me perhaps five whole minutes to do the job, but you'd be amazed how many weeks of time can pass in five minutes when you're the guy in the tank.

The shaft dropped in the hole with a THUNK, and the top of the tank shook. The sound was deafening, but it marked my success.

Immediately, I reached out the hatch, and a pair of hands pulled me out into the cold, and now, painfully bright room. I was hauled out of the hatch dripping with hot sticky peanut butter that now covered every single inch of my entire body except for my face.

The small group of perhaps a dozen guys had grown to well over two dozen men (and a few women) when I came out of there, and they all applauded and cheered like I'd just taken the stage at Woodstock. Every single person in the whole damn shop, even all of the workers from the assembly lines, had come running to see the freakshow. The whole damn factory was at a standstill just to watch my stupid ass emerge naked and covered in slimy peanut butter from that tank. I cannot begin to express how sincerely thankful I am that this happened back in the early '90s before everyone walked around with a camera in their pocket.

I marched my dripping, skinny, shivering, naked ass all the way to the other end of the facility where I was able to get hosed off. By the time I'd gotten there, about a block and a half in total, the peanut butter had hardened and I was scraping it off in gobs. The moment it got hit with the hose though, it became a strange combination of hard, waxy, greasy, and even more disgusting. Eventually, I was able to get to some manner of reasonably clean.

Getting the peanut butter out of my hair was a nightmare that lasted several more showers, however, it came with a weird upside - my hair felt amazing.

My shoes, however, would never be quite right again.

I got dressed, and now that I wasn't buck naked and dripping with shit, I got to ride on the little electric cart back to the other end of the factory. The machine was running in full swing and eating blocks of peanut butter at a rate of about three a minute. The line was happy, the client was happy, dad was happy, and everyone in the whole place had enjoyed the most memorable line upgrade in their history.

To this day, I cannot eat peanut butter.

But, I'll never forget to test the phasing on my motors again!

2

OUBLIETTE

The thing about discovery and learning is that it's a one-way road. You can't unlearn what you discover. Sometimes knowledge is a curse. Some lessons, though useful, are to remain as scars on your memory.

This is not a pleasant story.

The early two-thousands were a heyday for urban exploration in Kalamazoo, Michigan. With a trifecta of abandoned paper mills covering millions of square feet, the city was a haven for those of us who enjoyed wandering the pulp dust dystopia of an industrial wasteland left forgotten.

They would all be torn down in a few years, built into new neighborhoods, industrial parks, and yet another fucking microbrewery, but for now, they were lost in the bureaucracy of the superfund process and cascading quietly through CERCLA. We were kings of shady castles, and together we explored rusted wonders and tempted fate with treacherous rotting floors and asbestos as we wandered the shadows inside these ghosts of capitalism, long left abandoned.

The process of making paper is a very wet and goopy

affair. The majority of the entire factory was dealing with something much more like runny oatmeal than the sheets and rolls of paper that you're used to seeing. There were great forests of giant tanks, tubes, vats, and digesters that made up the entire central section of each paper mill.

A few of these were gleaming stainless vessels, but most mills dated back the better part of a century, so the majority of the larger tanks weren't even made of metal. While most of the stainless vats had been long removed, their scrap value far too tempting for the meth-heads and parasites, the giant concrete vats still remained. They formed massive empty secret bunkers, a part of the skeleton of the industrial paper mill that had lasted into this century.

These tanks were basically giant earthen silos, made of concrete and set deep. They rested on the basement level with their tops some twenty feet high - level with the first or second floors of the mill. They were lined in old brown tile with smooth walls, the only feature inside resembled a large ship's propeller near the bottom. These propellers ranged in size from as small as a foot or so to well over a yard in diameter. They were simply used for mixing, but when in use, created a tempest in a tank, shredding and homogenizing the pulp mixture before it was pumped down the pipe to the next process. Essentially, a giant blender.

In their day, these tanks never saw anything other than a thick liquid pulp of cellulose and water, so the only way in or out of the tank was through pipes. The largest of these pipes was as big as six or eight inches. However, on most of the tanks, there was an access hatch at the top. This was a square hole, usually about two or three feet square, set flush on the floor above the tank. Each hatch had a small concrete curb around it, a few inches high, lined with the same brown tile as within.

The hatch was necessary for tweaking mixtures, as the formula for a particular batch may require adding a few bags of various chemicals, pigments, or whatnot.

Up on the floor level, around the hole, would normally be a handrail made of the typical steel tubing painted yellow. While it would be nearly impossible to avoid slipping on the eternally wet floor of the mill, the handrail and the concrete curb would prevent workers from falling inside.

But now, decades later and after the scrap guys took what corrosion and time hadn't, those safety rails were often long gone. This left the small, protecting curbs to become ankle-breaking trip hazards, and it turned those old access hatches into death traps.

We called them, Oubliettes.

Any unsuspecting explorer who ventured through the mills had to remain watchful of these.

Because to fall into one left you alone, in the dark, in a smooth-walled dungeon twenty-feet down from a dim square... with no way out. You'd probably survive the fall with just a broken arm or leg, but nobody would ever hear you yell for help. Aside from the odd explorer or random homeless guy, nobody was likely to find you in time. You'd starve to death, in a puddle of your own filth, and the echoes of your screams.

We made a habit of checking in these holes when we passed by - just shine a flashlight down and have a quick look. There were dozens of them scattered across the giant complex, especially in mills C and D of the old, abandoned Allied Paper plant. Typically there was nothing down there but the crusty dust of pulp residue.

Sometimes people would throw random things down the holes, or set fire to something and toss it in. Over our years of exploration, we found various bits of trash and debris down in the oubliettes. Sometimes you'd find one that had been burned heavily, the pulp residue on the walls blackened. A few times the beam of my flashlight found remains of dead animals down on the bottom.

But on a cold afternoon in February of 2001, my light shone upon the thing I had always looked for and prayed never to find.

A body.

That's what it looked like at least - a man, slumped over, resting against the shaft of a large stainless propeller at the bottom of a thirty-foot tank under Mill D. There was no way to see clearly enough to be certain, but we were pretty sure. We gave a few shouts but nothing moved or responded. We discussed our options and formed a plan over a cigarette break at the mouth of the hole while peering down our flashlight beams trying to gain some level of certainty at what we feared we were looking at.

We had to do something, but our being in there wasn't exactly legal in the first place, so we weren't just going to call the cops and point it out for them. We ran home and ate lunch while we grabbed some climbing gear. I brought two rope bags of fat static line, my trusty old harness, and a rack of biners, ascenders, and etriers. I tossed the gear in the back of my car, with a six-foot length of thick towing chain, and we headed back.

It was quick work to set up an anchor from one of the massive I-Beams that held the roof up and rap down into the hole. It was the first time I'd worn a harness over a pair of Carhartts but it worked surprisingly well. With two guys up on top and an extra line hanging unused, just in case, I laced my rescue-8 and carefully dropped into the darkness.

The smooth tile wall was a few inches too far away for me to brace against, so I slowly spun in place, trying in vain to keep my headlamp fixed on the lump at the bottom of the tank. The only thing I could do was focus on the floor below me and make sure my landing was clear. It only took perhaps twenty seconds to make my way down and be standing on the bottom, but it felt like half an hour. I certainly wasn't in any hurry...

I softly touched down, and the first thing I was thankful for was that I had my radio. The guys were only thirty feet away, but talking was useless and shouting was insufferable. The echo inside the tank was fierce and deafening for anything above a whisper.

The second thing I noticed was that despite being February, in Michigan, it seemed to be ten degrees colder down here than outside. I scanned the floor and quickly found what I was looking for.

It was a man, well... most of him.

He looked about fifty years old, but homelessness brings a weathered look to people that belies their true age. The name on his blue work-shirt said "Dan", but it's pretty likely that was just a shirt he found in one of the locker rooms of the mill. He wore a light, blue-grey jacket, so he'd been down here since before it got too cold. He was gaunt, sunken, and the rats, raccoons, and opossums had made off with a few pieces of him. What was left of him was frozen solid.

I radioed the team and they tied a carabiner to the end of a roll of bright yellow "CAUTION" tape and dropped it down the hole. I tied it to the propeller shaft and clipped the biner on my rack before rigging up my ascenders and starting for the hatch.

I whispered, "I'm sorry, Sir," and said a silent prayer as I made my way, tediously, up the rope and back into the light. I don't know exactly what he went through, but I knew enough of his story to know it wasn't good.

As I came up through the hatch into the warm blinding light of a room that was dim and foreboding when I'd last left it only a few minutes before, I felt a wave of relief and thankfulness for simply getting out of that tank. I realized that feeling was a tiny fraction of the relief that Dan would never know. He must have been down there for days, maybe even weeks, before he laid against that propeller shaft and simply gave up his fight.

None of us said a word as we packed up the ropes and quietly walked to the nearest door, unspooling the caution tape as we went.

An anonymous call to the Sheriff's office from the payphone outside the bar at the end of the street told them of the dead homeless man that could be found by following the tape tied to the door handle of the southeast entrance to Mill D.

I don't know the details beyond that, but two weeks later we passed by the same hole again, and he was gone. The remnants of a large crowd of footprints were there in the dust on the floor. It must have been a fair circus involved in getting him out.

Be careful when you tread in abandoned places and keep

caution when you seek your adventures.

Gravity never sleeps, and I would rather never find you, frozen, alone, and trapped in the dark of your own oubliette.

Be curious, and by all means explore, but never, ever, do so alone. Keep your wits about you and stay safe out there.

3

I'M NOT UGLY

We'd been together for a few months, casually dating. Nothing terribly serious, just one of those easy, relaxed relationships of simple friendship where we occasionally traded orgasms.

We were barely through that first phase of any couple - the New Relationship Energy and all our guards were starting to come down. We were almost to the stage where she would start to fart in my presence, but not quite.

We thought we were being edgy, daring to tell our embarrassing truths to each other, and still too naive to realize that those exact same truths are common to almost everyone.

She was on her back, and I was kissing my way down her belly when she asked me, "Do you think I'm attractive?"

I tried to overlook the fact that she was asking this to a man who was laying on her bed, kissing his way down her naked body.

"Of course I do, you're intelligent, sexy, and have curves in all the right places. That's a silly question." I said, punctuating my sentences with kissing my way over her mons.

And then, because of fairness perhaps? Because of balance in the universe? I'll never know, but I raised my head and said, "How about me? Do you think I'm attractive?"

"Well," she said, "You're not ugly."

4

THE BEARING RACE

The greatest argument against evolution is that the average man survives puberty.

It was a miserable, blustery, autumnal evening in the early 2000s. Three of us were working late into the evening finishing up processing a massive donation of some corporation's junk. See, that's one of many shitty parts of owning a nonprofit; companies often use you as a trash service.

Pretty much everything you think you know about the administrative side of the nonprofit world is made of spin, marketing, or outright bullshit. Nobody wants to say this, and it's career suicide for anyone who actually works in the industry to call them out on their fuckery, but that's just how it is. Here's one of a million examples.

Companies, and I mean a lot of them, often donate equipment to various non-profits. Shit rolls downhill, and with the glorious power of a 501(c)(3) certification, you now have the ability to empower someone with a tax write off when they give you just about anything as a donation.

Now, this is great for things like giant checks and foundation support, but those are incredibly rare. The problem is, people have figured out how to use these deductions by donating outright trash, and that turns many nonprofits into disposal centers. Volunteer at any small place in your local community sometimes and you'll see the absolute garbage that people drop off at Churches, Youth Centers, and many thousands of other nonprofits.

Countless thousands of hours of human lives have been pissed away sorting through truckloads of other companies' trash hoping to find anything useful. It's a giant scam and a level of heinous fuckery most foul - here's how it works.

The value of anything is a matter of how it's perceived, and perception is everything.

Let's say, you've got a giant industrial machine. It's some highly specialized piece of process equipment that is a major component of your production line. Now, to the original manufacturer that was a hand-made, mission-specific, one-of-a-kind piece. They spent years developing it, and it took a team of forty people two months to assemble. It had to be shipped in pieces, and a team of half a dozen highly trained techs had to fly out to meet the delivery trucks and spend a week putting all the modules together on-site. At the end of the day, the bill comes in the mail, the bottom line says: Total Cost $12,000,000.

Fifteen years later, that machine has been operating for 130,000 hours, assuming a little downtime for maintenance. It's as worn out as a Catholic vagina. Originally, a priesthood of supernerds were flying out to do repairs and maintenance. After 8 years of that, the bean counters started to piss and moan so much about the cost that the service contract was allowed to expire. By then, the in-house techs had a pretty solid idea of how things worked, so they took over maintenance. They didn't have all the secret manuals or access to just the right parts, but they made do.

Then it got old enough to start being in line for replacement, and maintenance pretty much halted altogether. By this point, it's held together with Thoughts and Prayers, and the only reason it still functions at all is like a horny Nun - out of habit.

So, their bean counters, who have never set foot on the shop floor and couldn't actually find the machine if you parked it on their left nut, say that according to their depreciation tables it's now worth precisely fuckall. They've got justification to get a shiny new one, but these guys will look at a dead crack-whore and think "she's still warm enough for one more go fellas!" So, they get it appraised.

The appraiser (which is the German word for "Bullshit Artist who had too much of a soul to go into sales") shakes his magic 8-Ball, smacks a stained Ouija board on his abacus, and reads the bones of a roadkill raccoon in the bottom of his morning coffee cup until he has a Grand Mal seizure. When he wakes up, with the drool foam puddled under his face laying on the 220 grit, gray, commercial carpet of his office in the fecal position, the voices in his head that know the price of everything and the value of nothing tell him it's worth $1.48 Million on the surplus market.

So, they list it at auction. After three rounds it fails to meet the minimum bid of $500k. Because the only three other companies on Earth that could actually use the machine either already have a better one of their own, or they're so far away that the shipping for something the size of a school bus isn't worth it.

That's when the bean counters call a local nonprofit. Now, we don't give a shit about the machine itself or what it is, to us, it's a pile of parts. But, we like parts, and parts are expensive. So, we say "Fuck yeah!" and tell them where to drop it off. Hell, if they're close we send our own team out to dismantle it for them and spend a week hauling it back to our shop in pieces. All at our own cost, of course. The company could easily donate to help support our expenses in all this, but they don't because they just gave us a "twelve-million-dollar custom machine!"

So we haul the whole damn thing, in thousands of pieces, back to our shop. It has to go in an isolated room to be quarantined while we sort through the parts and inventory the whole damn pile. Every piece has to be itemized, and a rational "fair market" value has to be established. Often this is done by a few assholes with a laptop looking up each part on eBay for the "previously sold" listings.

Pages, countless pages of inventory are generated for the donation. Every power supply, switch, control panel, actuator, servo - the whole damn thing. Every single part that we can identify and get a price for is cataloged. The process is exhausting, tedious, and a monumental waste of fucking time. At the end of it, we now have a whole file folder of meticulously created values and supporting documents, a whole file folder that nobody will ever read.

The machine is now sorted into various piles. Anything that's useful goes into our supply inventory. Anything that's good, useful to someone, but we can't see any application for in the next calendar year, is sold as surplus so we can get fundraising out of it. All of the rest, anything that we can't use ourselves or sell to someone who can, that's scrap metal.

Almost nothing goes in the dumpster, not because of

some warm and fuzzy environmental reasons, but because dumpsters are expensive. Why pay $300 for a dumpster when you can get pennies on the pound for scrap?

To the scrap man, the bits of the machine that were left over from us? $5100.

The detailed, itemized paperwork we generated of all the parts? That came out to $147,218.

So… what was the machine actually worth? The donor is going to get a million and a half in tax write-offs because their appraiser said it's worth $1.48 Million. We don't get to determine that value, the donor's appraiser does. In the real world, we might get enough out of it to cover the light bill this month - if we're lucky.

As icing on the cake, the donor's PR team gets to talk about the "multi-million-dollar donation of custom equipment to a local non-profit". In actuality, we worked our asses off cleaning out a piece of their trash, so that we could immediately turn around and hand what little we could get squeezing blood from that stone over to the giant, local power monopoly so that they didn't turn our shit off for one more month.

This is the glamorous life of working in the nonprofit world.

After many hours of this, we were all at that stage of mentally exhausted where you just get a little loopy and stupid. Given that we had ready access to high voltage and power tools it really was just a matter of time before something stupid happened. Moments like this are why nights at the shop are storied and entertaining. It's what often made those nights worthwhile.

On this particular occasion, I was ass-deep in a pile of antique PLC devices, sorting them by model number. Mikey was sorting an old wooden crate filled with bearings and pillow blocks. Sean turned to him and recited the ancient incantation that has been used to summon the mischief demon into labs and workshops the world over since times immemorial:

"Dude! Wanna see something cool?"

At that moment, every head in the room prairie-dogged and turned to see exactly what manner of stupid was about to take place.

Sean grabbed one of the hundreds of new-old-stock bearings from the pile, opened the box, and dropped the wax paper wrapper on the floor as he jauntily marched over to the retractable hose reel on the wall with the look of chuffed self-assurance of someone who knows something awesome that you don't.

He held the inner race pinched wide in his fingertips and pointed the air gun at the bearings. With a pull of the trigger, the bearing screamed like a turbine engine spooling up. The outer race was spinning at fractional Mach when he opened his fingers and let it drop.

The moment it hit the floor it showered sparks out its ass like a drunken frat boy on the fourth of July and quickly took off towards the nearest wall. It started slowly but built speed exponentially as it balanced out its own friction and inertia of the smooth steel casing against the epoxied floor of the shop. It was a magnificent demonstration of basic physics known to anyone who has worked in a shop for a few years where bearings and compressed air are common.

Mikey thought this was the greatest thing since tits and explosions; he had to try it for himself. He ran across the room, picked up the two-inch bearing from where it had come to rest behind a fire extinguisher by the door, and ran back to where Sean and I were standing already holding out his hand for the air gun.

"I wanna try!" he said as he bounced on the balls of his feet with the gleeful joy of an idiot who has no idea he's about to nearly die.

I was standing on the wrong side to see it, but Sean took a couple of steps back. Without even being conscious of it, I followed suit. Mikey, who apparently didn't understand how a fucking wheel works, was holding the air gun to the bottom of the bearing instead of the top. He didn't realize he was spinning it up in reverse.

It was easily spinning over ten thousand RPM when it hit the floor...

I wish I could say that he was dumb but lucky and that it shot between his feet, scared the hell out of us all, and ended up on the wrong side of the room.

But, his shoe was in the way. The only thing that saved his life was that he was wearing big, chunky leather boots.

The unguided gyroscopic death wheel hit the floor and bounced, shooting yellow sparks out a few feet ahead of us, and then immediately proceeded to climb up his left foot.

It was at that moment that Mikey realized, he fucked up.

By nothing short of an actual, tangible, miracle of God almighty, the bearing somehow didn't touch his baggy jeans or his untucked shirt and missed his head by a cunthair as it launched up, just inches over his shoulder.

That's when the yelling started.

"You FUCKING RETARD!" I said with the gentle, caring, paternal nature of the shop elder as I walked over to get a new bearing. By now, the old one was lost somewhere back in the supply warehouse.

I grabbed a box at random from the pile and opened the shiny new bearing, about two inches in diameter with an open face like the last one. I picked up the air gun off the floor and gave a simple demonstration to Mikey on how to hold the nozzle at the proper angle and aim it at the balls, not the races. I also showed him how changing the airstream from the top or bottom changes the direction of rotation. We heard the bearing spin up, slow down, reverse, and back several times. We were all having fun with the sounds it made.

"Now watch this, and realize how close you just came to killing yourself by putting that fucking thing in reverse," I said, as I walked across the room and pushed the open button on the fourteen-foot-high overhead door at the back of the shop.

We were about forty feet inside the shop, behind the high-voltage cage where the giant Tesla Coil slept silently. We faced the door, and I spun up the bearing with the poise and confidence of someone who had done this since his dad taught him the stupid trick decades before.

I pulled the trigger, spun the bearing up to as fast as I dared hold it in my hand, and dropped it.

Inertia held it for the first bounce and with a couple of

sparks the second one bit enough to get it moving. By the time it was across the room, it was heading through the door at well over a hundred miles an hour.

Oh, FUCK.

The fourth rule of shooting safety is to, "know your target and beyond." It so happens, that rule applies to bearing racing too.

With a streak of sparks, it shot into the night, across the parking lot, and vanished. We couldn't see where it ended up, but we certainly *heard* it - large, plate-glass windows make a very distinctive sound when they shatter.

The difference between being a child and a grownup is that when you're an adult and you do something stupid, you run ***towards*** the sound of the breaking glass.

It had blasted through the front window of the autobody and detailing shop across the street. The window was about six feet square, and the entire upper third of it was pulverized, lying in pieces on the floor inside. The bearing was nowhere to be found.

It was well after ten o'clock, our lab and the auto shop were the only two businesses on the edge of a residential neighborhood and there were houses everywhere. Someone had to have heard that, or we probably set off their alarm system. We knew the cops would be arriving presently. So we all stood around with our thumb up our ass for a full fifteen minutes in weather where the air hurts your face, and none of us had grabbed a fucking coat on our way out.

"Fuck this bullshit, nobody's coming," Sean said, and started back across the street to the lab.

"Well we've got to do something, we can't just leave it like that," I said, jogging to catch up with Mikey on my heels.

We got inside and all found our coats. Moments later we were scrounging through the supply room looking for something to patch up the window. We had steel sheet metal, but it was way too long and we didn't want to cut it down for this. So we settled on a large sheet of Lexan that had spent its former life as the front panel safety guard on a labeling machine in a smoked sausage factory. It was a quarter-inch thick and about five feet square, with a shrug of "it'll do!" we proudly marched it out of the supply room and back into the main workshop.

I sent Mikey off to the tool room to get a roll of aluminum tape, and we all met up back across the street - now properly dressed for the weather. There wasn't a cop to be found.

With the grace, poise, and silence of a confused rhinoceros trying to rage-fuck a Volkswagon to a crygasm, our elite team of specialists worked diligently into the night. It took another trip back across the street to find some landscaping plastic for the top edge, but we made it alright and while it looked like a hickey on a hemorrhoid, it would at least keep the heat in and any particularly unmotivated thieves out until the morning.

We left a note taped to the inside of the window with a brief explanation, admission of guilt, and my phone number before we all headed off, exhausted and hungry. After a few minutes to have a cigarette and bullshit about the lessons learned that day, we all headed home.

The owner of the shop called me shortly after six-thirty the next morning. I was almost awake enough to remember that six-thirty happens twice a day. I was unhappy about this fact, but he was far more unhappy about his window and had the advantage of being conscious enough to form complete sentences, though only ones made entirely of capital letters.

I explained that I would be calling the glass repair place the moment they opened and would, of course, cover all expenses. That placated him, and I went back to sleep.

By ten-thirty that morning I was standing in fresh snow outside of his shop and enjoying the show as the two guys from the glass company lifted the nice, new piece of glass from their weird-looking truck into place on the front of his office. The autobody shop owner and I spent fifteen minutes talking about the odds, and how often it must happen, that a rock or something gets kicked up by a tire and breaks a new piece of glass because they drive down the road with the panels hanging on the outside of the truck. At no point in any of this conjecture did we actually bother to ask the guy that drives the damn truck, and I've gone twenty years since this happened and never gotten the answer.

In the end, I paid $450 for a new window, and Mikey got a lesson in physics, safety, and responsibility. The neighbor was happy, we all had a good laugh about it, and we all went back to finishing up the inventory for that giant donation.

The bearing was found that morning. It was still traveling with enough energy when it hit the back wall of his office to put a sizable dent in the front of his steel filing cabinet. He kept it, and it has sat on the desk in his office ever since. It's a paperweight with a good story.

5

THE EBS SYSTEM

I fucking love the power of swearing. I was raised in the blue-collar world of construction workers, railroad workers, Emergency Medicine, and championship alcoholics. These motherfuckers know how to swear at an Olympic level. It's in my genes.

However, my family wreath has given rise to a great dichotomy. This spectacular chasm of polarized contrariety throughout my professional life has allowed me to develop a skill that some of my close friends consider a minor superpower.

Because despite my innate and comfortable ability to embrace the power of the "colorful metaphor" as Spock once called it, my career choices have almost universally had me at odds with my colorful language. I've spent my entire life On Air, on camera, or in front of a crowd that often includes not only the wee precious children but their tight-assed helicopter parents as well.

As a result of that, I've developed a remarkable level of control of my tongue. The moment it's time to go live, I can simply turn it off.

What most of my friends don't know, is that there's a

reason for that. It was a powerful lesson I learned at the tender age of 17. It's not a superpower; it's a scar in my brain.

This is the story of that lesson.

I have always been a weirdo, and I got an early start. I was an outcast teenager and spent the majority of my time alone in my basement bedroom. A room that consisted of a twin-sized bed, a chest of drawers, and the remainder was filled with a sedimentary mountain of audio equipment. It ran the entire spectrum from professional broadcast and studio gear to "mom's old stereo," and it was perched on homemade shelves, a couple of dilapidated old desks, and a table that in a former life was a kitchen door -two houses ago.

I had acquired all of this over years of diligent scrounging. My first real mixing console came from the one and only music store that ever graced downtown Coopersville. I paid $100 for it, and the owner of the store had no idea it had taken me months of pushing a broom at the local feed mill to save up that much. Both the mill and the music store are long since gone, but the owner of that store and I are friends to this day.

I crossed the line into having a "real studio" once I could do actual multi-track recording. A dear friend gifted me a gigantic TEAC four-track reel-to-reel tape deck that weighed nearly as much as I did. His friendship, and that old tape deck, are still treasures to me today. Though technology has grown by leaps and bounds, and today I record on hard drives, that old tape deck still works and has held a place of honor in every studio I've owned across my entire life. It's been used in some part, however small, on every album that's ever been recorded, by every single band that's ever worked in one of my studios.

But it all started out in my bedroom "studio". Thanks to a nearby university scene, I produced a million basic "demo tapes" for local bands that nobody has ever heard of. I recorded Station IDs for all the tiny, low-budget radio stations that I could make a friend at. For the first year or so I did all the work for free. Partly because I wanted to build a resume and experience, and mainly because I really had no idea what the hell I was doing.

I got better, quickly, and started doing Bumpers and PSA's. I even got to start doing work for a few slightly larger stations, ones that people actually listened to. There are a million things that get played on the radio that aren't music. Most of these things are the boring, administrative side of radio and are usually made in-house at the station. Typically the people who do it for a living view them as a chore to produce and would rather be doing the "real" part of their job, which was usually being an On-Air jock. I had a pretty awesome time getting minuscule amounts of money to produce a ton of things that nobody wanted to make anyway.

I did it for everyone I could get to answer a phone. Some people hired me based on the fact that I worked for practically nothing, but most did it because I was a fourteen-year-old kid, and they just wanted to be kind and give me a shot. I was thrilled to be doing real studio work, and it sure as hell beat pushing a broom at the feed mill.

I remember the exact, magical moment I first heard my own voice on the radio. I was riding in the van to school (yeah, I was one of those short-bus kids). The driver was an incredibly beautiful young woman with a blonde pixie cut. She used to play Top-40 music because we all liked it, and it kept us quiet on the long drive.

The clock swept the bottom of the hour. Just for a moment, as Aerosmith faded out and in the instant before the commercial started, the whole van was surprised to hear my voice say "One Oh Four Point Five, The New Sunny FM! WSNX, Holland, Grand Rapids". I let out a squeal like I had just won a Grammy. The driver turned to look at me and said, "That was you?!" I was thrilled. I WAS ON THE RADIO!

I earned my "Golden Ticket" shortly after my fifteenth birthday. At the time, I was the youngest person in the USA to hold one, though my record has long since been shattered and I believe the current record holder is actually a five-year-old in LA.

I have no idea how the system works these days, but way back then you needed an actual federal license to be a Disc Jockey and be allowed to talk on the radio. It's a yellow piece of paper, the same shape and a bit bigger than a dollar bill that says "Federal Communications Commission Radiotelephone Operator Permit". They weren't hard to get. The "test" was quite possibly written by the station manager himself and the hardest question on it was trying to remember the date. I'm sure it was just a basic matter of course for everyone who signed up as a DJ to get one, but to me, you'd have thought it was a Ph.D. for as proud as I was of having earned it.

My mom framed it because that's what moms do.

I got an unpaid gig doing an evening show on a tiny 100 Watt low-band, nonprofit FM station that had just moved into their "big new studio". The new studio had one On-Air booth, a lobby just big enough for four people to stand in, an indoor outhouse, and a manager's office that I never once saw anyone occupy. The whole place was various shades of ugly 70's brown and could have passed for a tired Dentist's office if it wasn't for all the stale cigarette smoke that emanated from the walls.

Their previous studio had been a closet in a building downtown, and you had to do your shows with the door open. You had to keep your stack of records on the floor in the hall because there wasn't enough room inside. I got lucky and never saw the old place. I was one of the first on the team for the new studio. They had just expanded their hours and would take anyone with a pulse, so I qualified.

The booth was comfortable and familiar. Everything that was "professional" grade was twenty years old. All of the nice new stuff looked like it came from someone's home stereo. It was a motley collection of mismatched garbage held together with questionable engineering. The whole place was made with dodgy soldering and random unlabeled Radio Shack project boxes that did God knows what. My bedroom studio was more well equipped.

The room was about twelve feet square. The West wall had a door and a big window that looked out into the dark lobby. The only other window was on the East wall, and just featured a parking lot of the place next door. Inside, the booth was dominated by a pair of large old desks arranged in an L. The main console sitting in the middle of the left desk, facing a featureless wall of brown fake wood paneling and a small TV mounted up near the ceiling that was supposed to be showing the weather channel.

The main console was an antique behemoth with a single row of big rotary knobs and a handful of switches that usually worked, most of the time. It was flanked by a stack of gear on either side, cassette decks, CD players, and Cart machines. Everything was in pairs so that you could cue things up while live and ping-pong back and forth.

To the right, under the outside window, was the second desk. It held a pair of turntables that were old enough to be my grandparents'. To the right of that, sitting in the corner, was a proper 19-inch equipment rack that was taller than I was. The rack held the uplink to the transmitter, the Emergency Broadcast box, and a pair of three-ring binders, one red, the other white.

The white book was the transmitter log. We had to pick up the phone every few hours and call the transmitter, which was located at the bottom of a water tower a few miles away. You gave it a gentle touch of tones, and a robotic voice would tell you the numbers for things like how many watts of power you were broadcasting at that moment. It was the duty of the DJ to record these numbers diligently so that they could go in the book and never be read by anyone ever again.

The red book was the Emergency Broadcast System manual. In the event of nuclear war or tornadoes, it would tell you exactly what to do for the last five minutes of your life.

Cascading to the floor and joining the back of both desks was a black waterfall of tangled cables that all looked the same. God have mercy on anyone who disturbed the cable monster.

The fact that any of it worked at all was a miracle, and only the "engineer" who built it had any clue HOW it worked. But through a long chain of magic and physics, when I pressed the play button on the CD player sitting here, a whole city of people and I could listen to the music together.

I was enchanted.

My show ran Tuesday nights from Midnight to 2 am, because I was the FNG (Fuckin' New Guy) and got the slot that nobody else would take. I didn't care; I was the last show on the air at night. Nobody actually told me that I had to shut the station down on schedule, and that meant that I could run as long as I wanted. My actual showtime usually ran until dawn when Al would come in and start his shift, a Jewish morning show called "Hatikva!" at 7 am. It gave me just enough time to pack up my milk crate of tapes and CDs and get to school before class started.

It wasn't long before I had worked out a solid groove and was absolutely comfortable on my long nights of being a fifteen-year-old kid completely in charge of an entire radio station. The only time I ever saw anyone else at the station was if one of my weirdo friends came to hang out. Usually, they were all sound asleep while I kept the gas station clerks, third-shift factory workers, and tow truck drivers mildly entertained and jamming through the night.

I had no format, style, or shtick. My entire show consisted of playing whatever music I felt like from my own massive collection of CDs, and talking about the music, the stories behind the bands, and the songs. I have an encyclopedic and fundamentally useless knowledge of music. I played the stuff that I liked and taught the things that I knew. My brother-in-law, Tony came up with the name of my show. We called it The Molotov Cocktail Hour, and it fit.

I never really cared who, or how many, actually listened. I was talking to the whole city, or at least the tiny fraction of people who were awake. My show was never promoted, and I never did any marketing except for the one time when I accidentally printed forty-thousand business cards and passed them out to everyone I could. It was simple, and there was a purity to the performance. Just a kid who was sharing his passion with anyone who cared to listen.

My show did well, and my audience steadily grew. We didn't have ratings or anything, and I measured my viewership by how many phone calls I got during the show. This was long before anyone outside of a research lab had email, so people had to actually call me if they wanted to talk.

I held my steady time slot (because nobody else was dumb enough to ever want the graveyard shift) and had a ton of fun. I would take chances and do things no other DJ was doing. Having such a long show let me do things like play an entire album with no breaks, and then spend the next hour talking about its history, the band, the recording process, and all the little trivia that went with it. People loved it, and I became a staple among the third shift factory workers of the Westside.

I also became popular with local music nerds for a cool reason. This was back when people got a lot of new music by recording it off the radio, and I had a strict personal rule about never talking over the song I was playing. I kept a specific CD playing for voice-over music and would switch to that whenever I was talking. This made it possible for people to actually record music from my show, without my dumbass voice talking over the end of it. It's a simple thing, but wow did I get a ton of phone calls thanking me for doing it.

The best thing about working overnights in a shitty little radio station is that nothing ever happens. Except for the occasional visit from one of my weirdo friends or lovers, I never saw anyone until morning. It was dead quiet all night, and we were on the outskirts of town so there wasn't even any traffic. It was incredibly quiet and peaceful.

Most of the time.

I was seventeen, it was shortly after Midnight, and the rain outside was Vanilla Sex; fucking near horizontal. The window was rattling enough that you could hear it through my microphone. I was expecting the power to go out anytime and was playing "Big Generator" by Yes and making the best of a bad situation.

That's when the world exploded.

Just above and behind my right ear the Emergency Broadcast System box started screeching with the full-throated wild abandon of an autistic kid who just had his juice box snatched. If I ever meet the cocksucker who thought it was a good idea to rackmount 120-decibel alarm horn four feet from the DJ's ears, I'm going to wrap my dick around his neck and try to drop-start him like a fucking chainsaw.

The real problem wasn't that the box scared the living shit out of me, launching me out of my chair and onto my feet, ready to run out of the room in a moment of pure adrenaline and fear. No.

It was that I was between songs, talking live on the air when it happened.
In times of extreme duress, people instantly drop to the language of their upbringing. This is especially true for immigrants and on-air talent. I am no exception. Without a moment's reservation or hesitation, I brought forth a superlative string of expletives and invectives that would have every tightass, conservative biddy in the women's auxiliary clutching her pearls and blushing so hard she'd have a stroke right there at the bridge table.

I regained my composure after a few seconds, pulled the

binder off the rack, followed the EBS instructions to the letter, and was suspended for 30-days even before the fifteen-minute-long Tornado Warning had cleared. Big Al the station manager was pissed, and I was heartbroken.

My fellow jocks however are not without a sense of humor. A universal truth about DJs is that they're widely regarded as assholes - it comes with the job. If over the course of your life you've had more than five people begin a fight by saying "I'll bet you think you're fucking funny, don't ya?" it's probably a good idea to put together a tape and a resume. You're most likely DJ material.

Now, every one of my listeners heard my ten seconds of "WHAT THE FUCK IS THAT SHIT!". The substitute who filled my time slot the next week could have easily said "Chris was suspended for a month for swearing on the air, you're stuck with me for a few weeks." and go on with his day.
But no, of course, he didn't do that.

Because he wasn't just the typical asshole late-night DJ. This was a guy who had a personality that washed over you like an unwelcome wave of sweat when you're having a bad, late-night shit. He got on the air, opened my show, and proceeded to tell my entire listening audience that I had died in a car crash.

Because he's a cunt.

Now, all my friends knew better, so that was no problem. My parent's phone wasn't in the phone book. Remember, this was before the internet was a thing, people used phone books, not Google.

My grandparents' number, however, was the only listed number with my last name anywhere in the county.

My sainted, patient, meek grandmother completely lost her fucking mind when people started calling her with condolences. Several people even sent her flowers. She had herself well and truly un-fucking-hinged by the time she called my parents (a total of about five minutes after the flowers and phone calls started the next morning after the show).

Once she found out I was alive and well, she was absolutely prepared to kill me with her bare hands. Even years later, she thought this was some stupid stunt I pulled, and she never believed me when I told her I had nothing to do with it.

Even at the station people sent in cards and letters, a couple of people sent in mix tapes. It would appear the dorky kid on the radio all night long was more popular than I (and Al) had ever imagined.

I had to call Al and explain the situation to him. Al was more pissed at the other guy for what he pulled than he was at me for swearing on the air. At least I had an understandable reason for my actions. Al taught me a valuable lesson about good management, learn the difference between when you have a problem, and when your boss has a problem. Asshole DJ wasn't my problem, he was Al's.

Al was… displeased. He told me that he'd handle it, and he did in his characteristic style.

After a conversation that I would have bought tickets to hear, Al fired the Asshole DJ. He put me back on the air (two weeks early!), and now not only did I have my usual time slot, but I also had his as well! I was ecstatic because now I had a whole two nights a week!

I began my first show in his slot by informing the world that he was suffering from a debilitating bout of saber-toothed fire-breathing crotch crickets and would be gone for the foreseeable future.

Payback is a bitch. But you can bet your fuckin' ass I never swore on the radio again.

6

BARBEQUE SAUCE

And you wonder why I don't go to parties...

It was New Year's Eve in a year that wasn't a multiple of five, so nobody cared. I was doing what nerds typically do on such an obvious night for partying, sitting at home on my computer, and avoiding the world. I generally avoided recreational pharmaceuticals because I could never figure out if it's stupid people that do drugs, or if it's the drugs that make you stupid. Drinking was never a hobby of mine because I never considered puking my brains out and sleeping on someone's front lawn as my idea of "having a good time". That combined with my affinity for social awkwardness meant I've never really been one for the party scene.

So, the high point of my evening was the random cute blonde girl who started messaging me out of the blue.

I had responded to her ad on a now long-defunct dating website, and we gently hit it off. This evening was our first real conversation beyond initial pleasantries as our orbits came into alignment, and we spent several hours doing the delicate dance of seeing if any of our fundamental traits would instantly terrify or offend the other. The problem with online dating is that it's filled with people who are at a point in their life where they think online dating is a good idea.

She lived a state away, which was close enough for potential, but there was certainly no way I was going to be seeing her that evening. She could be Miss Right, but she wasn't going to be Miss Right Now. So, after several hours of chatting with her, I was delighted when another random person messaged me by surprise.

It turns out that even years later, both of these two people would have a notable impact on my life.

The second girl was the exact opposite of the first. In stark contrast to the statuesque, Scandinavian who lived in a different time zone, she was a petite, ebony girl who lived only a couple miles from me. We'd also never chatted before, but she was bored and had been invited to a New Year's Eve party. She didn't want to go alone and asked if I would care to join her. I wasn't terribly interested in being at a party, but she was cute as hell and with thoughts of "a bird in the hand..." I figured, "fuck it, why not". I politely ducked out of my conversation with the blonde and made plans to meet this second girl in hopes of getting my hand in her bush.

Now, you would think that given the disproportionate amount of emergency services calls to the rougher neighborhoods of Kalamazoo, the residents of such places would be more diligent about putting numbers on their damn houses. This, however, was not the case. That's how I ended up being the white guy in the wrong place for several blocks in any direction, cruising back and forth for half an hour wandering all over the hood trying to find the right house.

I parked my car and stepped out into the cold night air. It

wasn't the worst neighborhood in Kalamazoo, but it certainly wasn't the kind of place you want to just be wandering from house to house at nearly midnight. Thankfully, house numbers follow a consistent pattern: odd numbers on one side of the street, even numbers on the other. The whole neighborhood was just a set of giant number lines. With the confidence and motivation of a young, horny, college kid, I knocked on the door of what I had derived mathematically must be the right house.

It's not like I had google maps to tell me where to go - this was the early 2000's. This had to be the right house, I was certain of it. I was even more certain than I'd been at any of the previous half dozen houses I'd knocked at. The numbers in the next block were all in the five-hundreds while I was looking for an address in the four-hundreds. We'll just quietly overlook the fact that I was now over a quarter-mile from where I'd parked.

I put my hand up to knock on the door of the house I knew was the right one when she poked her head out of a second-story window across the street. With all the decorum and subtlety of a sledgehammer, she yelled for me to get my stupid ass inside before someone shot me in the face.

That was totally going to be the next house I would have knocked at. Totally...

I gingerly jogged across the street in that manner known to anyone who lives where the air hurts your face and the roads get slick with packed black ice.

Now, when someone invites you to a party, you hold a fundamental set of preconceived expectations. Usually rather high on that list is some manner of crowd, a gathering of perhaps a dozen people at the very least.

What I wandered into was a typical hood-rat habitat. The entryway was dominated by an old mattress leaning bent against the wall next to a long, steep staircase with no handrail and flakey, chipped lead paint of a condition that some daft bint basic bitch on Pinterest would someday call "distressed".

Still, I sojourned, onwards and upwards. The hopes of my dick leading the way...

There's a smell, in my entire life I've never been able to accurately describe it, but there's a particular smell. It's not quite the smell of a trash can that sat too long and went to maggots before being emptied and douched with bleach. It's that, but from across the room. It smells like a mid-'70s color palette of reddish-ochre, grimy mustard yellow, and stone-washed purple. It's subtle but sharp and pervasive. It's the miasma of poverty and neglect. It's the smell that comes after the last fuck to give has long since gone. It's like "old people smell", but for run-down houses. It's the mephitic smell of "not dead... yet" for a structure in the shitty part of town; it tells you that people still live there, but not for long.

I stepped through the open doorway at the top of the stairs to find a room, poorly illuminated from the sodium glow of a streetlight hanging just below the naked front windows. It was a disheveled, upper-level, low-rent apartment that took up the entire second floor.

Long ago, some enterprising fuckstick slumlord had kicked out the walls of what was likely only a bedroom, a bathroom, and a fair bit of attic and turned it into an apartment the moment he discovered the loophole that square footage was measured on the floor, not the ceiling. This means that you can remove all the full-height walls, push the room back into the attic and get a huge amount of new floorspace. The tradeoff is that you can't actually stand up in half the room. But who needs to hang art on the walls when you're already living in a Dali painting.

The whole place was one big open room that melded into a kitchen off to the left towards the back of the house, and three doors that lead to a bathroom, a bedroom, and what could laughingly be called a closet by someone with a level of optimism reserved for morning show hosts and fitness instructors. It was the kind of place where the moment you walk in, you get a good look around for potential exits.

The "party" was a group of six people (including myself), plus a few people in ones and twos across the room, and most of them were varying states of inebriated. It took me all of thirty seconds to realize that the only thing I wanted out of this place was me. I'd been there less than five minutes and had already spent two of them working on a polite exit strategy.

That's when the KPS disco lights started reflecting off the ceiling. I walked across the room just far enough to get a look outside and see four Kalamazoo Public Safety cop cars lined up on the other side of the street. They were getting out and started milling about the houses and backyards on the other side of the block. A couple of minutes later, a K9 unit arrived and joined in the fun. It occurred to me that they were probably looking for the suspicious asshole who was knocking on front doors a little while ago.

Thankfully my car was several blocks from there, but I sure as shit wasn't going to just wander outside and start hoofing it. Despite what the "copaganda" would have you believe, unless you're seven, white, and lost, the police are not your friends. There was nobody out there tonight but cops, drunks, and tow-truck drivers, and I was far too melanin-deficient to be wandering down this part of Douglas to not catch someone's eye at this time of night.

Well, shit.

Looks like I'm going to have to stay and enjoy the "party" for a little bit.

She walked over and introduced herself. For the first time, I got to meet my mysterious internet girl in person. She was short, about five-three, pert, perky, and firm with curves in all the right places. She had a perfect, blinding smile that would take me another decade of surgeries to catch up to. While mine cost as much as the college education neither of us would ever get, genetics had gifted her with perfection. Her big almond eyes could captivate a man's soul. She had an ass that was shaped like a perfect heart when she bent over, with a pair of dimples on her back so you knew exactly where to put your thumbs. Her nose was retrousse and her skin was Denzel-black; the whole package combined was breathtaking. She was staggeringly beautiful.

Right up until the moment that she spoke and shattered my dreams of having her ruin my life.

She would have been perfect were it not for the fact that she was as painfully stupid as a fishnet stuff sack full of thumbtacks precariously packed in your back pocket. After talking to her for less than five minutes, it was obvious that the smartest thing that would ever come out of her mouth was the head of my dick. She was vacuously, contagiously stupid, so dumb that I could feel myself losing IQ points merely by standing next to her. I was certain of this because having sex with her was starting to seem like a good idea.

I decided to embark on the most socially-awkward mingling imaginable, because talking to her was like masturbating with a belt sander, and I was already feeling rough enough.

I wandered across the room to a group of four people who were having a passionate discourse about something I couldn't hear well enough to make out. They were standing in a small circle close enough to touch each other and as I came up behind one of the girls she exclaimed, "I just don't like white guys!". I don't have any idea what the hell they were talking about before that, it was just background noise, but I caught that and started to giggle as I hung back just far enough to not engage the conversation.

A gentleman from across their group who was standing opposite of this girl, and facing me, stepped through the center and shook my hand. He had a sincere, gentle smile that started from his eyes, a soft deep voice that sounded like if a Cummins diesel could idle just above a whisper, and was roughly the size of a refrigerator with feet. He was over six feet tall, easily three-hundred pounds, and had the confidence of someone who was accustomed to being feared with the temperament of someone who didn't enjoy it. I liked him instantly.

"Ignore her - she's drunk," he said

"It's alright, I don't like a lot of white guys either," I said as we exchanged the upward head nod of friends in agreement, "I'm Chris".

"Curtis, call me CJ," the gentle giant replied.

"Pleasure to meet you, Sir."

CJ and I wandered the room and talked for twenty minutes. I told him about why the cops were holding a block party outside, and he filled me in on the basics of everyone in attendance. By the end of our lap of the room and our first conversation, we had been friends for twenty years. As we walked around he introduced me to everyone else in the room, except the one little group.

I noticed that every time he'd introduce me to someone he'd say, "This is Chris, he's alright," and if it was a guy he was introducing me to, they'd respond with an almost imperceptible upnod. I don't know if this was something he was conscious of or not, but it seemed like he was giving me the secret black guy seal of approval.

We walked back to the small group and CJ introduced them. First, there was Tamika, who doesn't like white guys. She was short, stacked, and would make for one hell of a meaningful weekend relationship. There was Nikki, who turned out to be the best friend of my original date for the evening and was clearly the brains of that pair. And there was LaVaughn, an anorexic giant who stood nearly seven feet tall, spoke with the breathlessness of Marilyn Monroe and a queer lilt that told the world he wasn't just out and proud, he was so fabulously gay that he actually sparkled. I'm pretty certain that if he farted it would sound like someone playing a moonshine jug.

I turned to Tamika and asked, "So, I'm frightfully curious, why don't you like white guys?"

I was expecting a discourse on the cultural divide, institutional racism, or men being pigs. She had hundreds of years of ammunition to drop on my head to give any one of a thousand intelligent and justified answers. She could have quoted Malcolm or King, taken me from a righteous woman in a Selma bus to Huey P. Newton, and

I'd have followed along just fine. She could have taken that in any one of a dozen directions, and I was prepared for any one of them. What I was in no way prepared for was what she actually said,

"They taste like chicken and that's fuckin' weird."

I blinked, and my eyebrows shifted to low beams as I side-eyed her, "Urm... what?"

"White guys taste like chicken, and it freaks me out," she said again, more matter-of-factly.

"Chicken?"

"Yep"

"Uh... Okay", I replied, because what the fuck else are you supposed to say to that?

Thankfully I was saved by LaVaughn who chimed in with, "Exactly how many white guys have you tasted, Tamika?" and everyone laughed.

"Just one - that was enough. White guys have tiny dicks and taste like chicken," she scowled.

"A chemist, a physicist, and a mathematician were on a train," I pontificated, "and had just crossed the border into Scotland."

Everyone stopped and looked at me like I was as high as giraffe pussy. I continued, "Just give me a moment, there's a point."

"The chemist looked out of the window, saw a black sheep for the first time in his life, and exclaimed, 'Look! Scottish sheep are black!'

The physicist said, 'No, no. Some Scottish sheep are black.'

The mathematician threw down the book he was reading and said. 'No, you fuckheads! In Scotland there is at least one field, containing at least one sheep, of which at least one side is black.'"

CJ smiled, LaVaughn smiled, Nikki smiled, and Tamika didn't get the fucking point as one of her brain cells was tossing the other one a life preserver in the tiny pond of ethanol that had flooded the otherwise empty space between her ears.

Thus began a heated debate on body types, shampoo, diet, body wash, and a great deal of time spent on being "ashy" where I tried in vain to understand exactly what the hell that was. I also learned of the importance of both Shea and Cocoa butter, though I got the impression that neither was part of a healthy diet. The end result of the conversation was that LaVaughn and Nikki were trying to goad Tamika into sucking my dick to prove that not all white guys taste like chicken. I was pretty damn sure they just wanted a floor show. Either way, I'm not a complete idiot, and any chance I get for either stupid penis tricks or a random blowjob - I'm there.

Nikki was clearly the instigator and roused enough rabble that ten minutes later Tamika was getting blindfolded in the bedroom by LaVaughn, while CJ and I were standing side by side in the middle of the kitchen. The plan was for Nikki to lead Tamika out and prove to her that she couldn't tell one from the other. I had no idea what to expect or which girl I was going to end up with by the end of the evening, but I was certainly happy to be along for the ride.

The three of them came out into the kitchen and Nikki pointed at CJ and said "You first, and don't talk. I don't want her being able to figure out who is who". He unzipped, unfurled, and as Tamika got to work while LaVaughn gave color commentary on her ability.

And judging by the show, she had ability. It only took her a few moments to have CJ at full-mast, and she was enthusiastic, to say the least.

Nikki pointed at me and twirled her finger. I took this as my cue to get ready. Thankfully the preceding floor show had already put me in a state so as to be just difficult enough to unfurl to be reasonably impressive.

With an unceremonious tap on the forehead, Nikki signaled CJ that his time was up and we shuffled into our new stations. Tamika didn't even flinch and dove in with abandon, only to immediately make an "OOMPTHPH" when she realized that sample B, while not quite as thick as the impressively girthy A, had substantially more length than she was expecting. Being motivated by the stereotype, she fell victim to her prejudice and proceeded to prove her point by performing with passionate fervor.

She was moaning and we were both having a hell of a great time for about thirty seconds, right up until she wrapped the base of my cock in her hand. Then, with all the same passion with which she'd been working, she shoved me back out of the moment.

"GAH!" she said, as she recoiled backward in disgust. She nearly fell over in the process as she ripped off her blindfold, spitting and cursing at both me and Nikki.

Nikki gave me a look that could have frozen an Eskimo's nuts off, clearly thinking I had whitened her smile or something. I shook my head and said, "No, no, I didn't do nothing".

It was the hair. None of us had taken into account the immediate and substantial differences in our pubic hair. When she had put her hand up, it brushed against my pubes and her mental image shattered.

Everyone in the room had one hell of a laugh, except Tamika. She was incensed. We had all just watched her go to town, clearly enjoying herself, only to fall victim to her prejudice. LaVaughn, the only guy in the room to not get his dick sucked, laughed harder than anyone and was having a field day with this fact. He was merciless, probably because he was the only one with nothing to lose.

CJ and I just stood there with our dicks hanging out, quietly hopeful, as the conversation continued.

Nikki and Tamika engaged in a heated debate over how she was an idiot and had proven herself wrong. This went on for a couple of minutes with Tamika being steadfast that it wasn't the difference in race but in taste, and that I most certainly tasted like chicken, etc. It was a dumb and circular argument and nobody got anywhere.

I was paying attention, interjecting as I could, in quiet hopes that I was going to get one or the other by the end of the evening when I was ripped screaming from that entire thought process by the sensation of something very cold happening on my most sensitive of places.

That motherfucker LaVaughn, who I had liked up until this moment, with a bit of whimsical impishness that was impressive for a gentleman of his stature, had taken advantage of my distraction to quietly retrieve a squeeze bottle of barbecue sauce from christ-knows-where in the kitchen. He had come up beside me and while I was arguing the finer points of prejudice being stupid as hell, that rat bastard squeezed a fat line of thick maroon sauce down the entire length of my cock.

I let out a yelp and jumped so high that we almost came eye to eye for a moment.

"What... the fuck... man?" I yelled as everyone in the room took a moment to laugh like hell.

"Well, if she's gonna bitch about you tasting like chicken, I figured I'd help her out and give it some flavor. There ya go girl, he's all set!" he said, gesturing to my cock like a game-show host.

I had just hit a new record for awkward uncomfortability, and on this evening, that was a pretty high fuckin' bar already.

CJ and I just stood there quietly commiserating while the rest of the gang all proceeded to torment Tamika. The conversation was lively to say the least, while CJ and I discussed the actual odds that either of us had any chance of actually getting laid that night. Things had been going so well on a nice predictable path, only to change from 2nd to reverse in a grinding flash.

I looked at Tamika who was still kneeling in front of us with Nikki sitting on the floor just behind her and said, "well at the very least you can help me clean this off". Tamika made a face that was somewhere between "ick, no" and that dumbass pouty, tantrum face that girls mistakenly think guys find cute. I was half hoping that Nikki may take actions into her own mouth.

What I was most certainly not fucking prepared for was LaVaughn to be a stealthy gay ninja, turn nearly 180 degrees, bend at the waist, and in one smooth movement without a moment's notice, reservation, or hesitation inhale my entire cock to the base and suck off the majority of the barbecue sauce in less than half a second.

I let out... well it could only be honestly described as a "shriek", but I assure you it was the manliest of shrieks and was in no way similar to the sound of a little girl who had just fallen off her tricycle. Not at all, it was quite manly, very becoming of a rugged gentleman such as myself, as I ran with everything I had. I ran out the door, down the rickety staircase, and was on the sidewalk before the cold reminded me to put my dick back in my pants. I ran the few blocks to my car and was home within ten minutes.

I got inside and could hear my roommate upstairs in the front bedroom doing her best to get pounded through the floor. Great, everyone was getting laid for New Years' but me.

I took a shower, scrubbed until I was nearly raw, and finally sat back down at my computer, where I probably should have stayed in the first place. I had several "Happy New Year" messages from friends near and far and worked my way down the list replying to them.

I came upon the message from the girl who had invited me out earlier that evening and immediately deleted it. I never heard from her again and didn't consider it any manner of loss.

I went to bed, and in the morning resumed my conversation with the tall, blonde science nerd in the neighboring state. I'm happy to report that one worked out a little bit better.

It's New Year's Eve as I'm writing this, and today is our 17th anniversary together.

This is why I don't go to parties…

7

THE PRESS BIT HIM, NOW HE CRIES

A print shop is a living, breathing beast of a room filled with things that will hurt you the moment you don't respect them. It's a well-balanced hurricane of noise and bustle with people all moving about doing a thousand things at once. It's the mental picture I always get when I hear some guy with a mid-Atlantic accent made of enlarged adenoids and unfiltered cigarettes in an old-time film talk about "Progress and Industry".

It's generally not considered to be the kind of place you get to see Heroes in action. But, life and industry are full of surprises. Sometimes those Heroes come in the form of a person you'd least expect.

Borz is one of them.

This fuckin guy - in his short-sleeved, button-down dress shirt and giant square '80s glasses that defined half his face - was the living, breathing definition of a nerd. Sure, his glasses had gone out of style a decade before, but he didn't give a shit. Borz didn't bother with fashion. He rocked a mustache that would make "Diabeetus" Brimley proud; he may have done this to hide the fact that he quite possibly had no upper lip at all. Borz has always been a "Form Follows Function," no bullshit kind of guy.

Borz owned being a nerd and was confident, capable, and cool. He gave no visual clues of being anything more than an old-school trades teacher who wasn't about to take any of your bullshit.

That's exactly what I thought of him anyways when I walked into his class as a high-school junior in the early '90s.

He was the instructor of the Printing/Graphic Arts class at the Tech Center, and like a hickey on a hemorrhoid, I was to become a bright and shiny pain in his ass. Everything you need to know to truly understand my relationship with Borz can be explained in the fact that during my second year in his class he changed the default error sound on every computer in the entire department to a loud recording of himself saying, "Boden, just leave the thing alone!"

And to think it all began with a clerical error.

I was originally enrolled in the Media Production class. I'd had some manner of recording studio in my parent's house since I was twelve, and that was the path I wanted to pursue. So, when I saw there was a class for recording and production, I thought it would be a natural fit. It was, in fact, the one and only reason I signed up for Tech Center in the first place. But the fickle finger of fate fucked me, and when I showed up for my first day of class I was directed to a totally different room.

Somewhere along the way, a computer had flipped a bit, a secretary had screwed up, or maybe God just decided the Borz needed to be punished. Whatever happened, I was magically assigned to the printing class. I was pissed. What the fuck do I want to learn about printing for? I don't care about printing. I don't want to waste years in a bullshit class that I'm never going to use to learn a trade I don't give a shit about. I went back to the office to bitch, and the poor secretary - who was tits deep in a thousand minor crises on the first day of classes - kindly asked me to just ride out the day and that tomorrow I'd be put back into the right class.

"Yes, Ma'am," I said, and walked quietly back to class.

It took only two hours of my first day with Borz to change my entire opinion on printing. The secretary kept her word and changed my class assignment the next day, but I never set foot in Media Production. I just kept going to Borz's class. They couldn't drag me away.

See, a print shop is a delight to the senses. There's nothing even close to compare it to, except maybe working in a chocolate factory. To this day, the smell of a printshop is one of the happiest memory triggers in my world. Everything in there has a distinctive smell, even the different printing processes have their distinct smells, from Offset to Flexo to Screen. It's incredible, and I loved it from the moment I walked in.

It's also loud as hell. If you've ever worked in a shop with an air compressor you get the idea. Only imagine twenty air compressors of all different sizes running at the same time in a room with thirty people. A printing press makes such a distinctive sound that there's actually a word for it. It's the onomatopoetic origin of the word "cliché".

Conversations happen at a respectable shout, like in a nightclub. The first time you step into the room it's intimidating as hell. After a week, you're not only used to it, but it becomes comfortable. Hell, I've had naps in the process camera darkroom.

The first thing you walked past as you entered the print shop was the large, old, battleship grey, Steelcase desk sitting just to the left as you step in the front door. This was Borz's desk, or at least, the desk that was ostensibly his. It was the spot that any teacher would have their desk, but in the three years I spent with Borz I never saw him sit down, much less man a desk. Borz isn't exactly the kind of guy who does "desk" work.

The desk was a catch-all for random shit and drawers were often left hanging open. One day I noticed a pair of absolutely gigantic, flat-head screwdrivers sitting in one of the side drawers. Each one was about eighteen inches long and had a shaft about half an inch thick. I'd never seen them used for anything, and all the other tools were spread around the shop. These two were clearly special. I pondered their existence for a moment, but quickly went on with my day and forgot about them.

At least, for the next year and a half...

I was cutting business cards on the hydraulic paper cutter - one of my favorite machines to operate. There's something about a machine that has a four-foot-wide razor blade with a thousand pounds of force behind it that just satisfies the reptile brain and makes my dangly bits tingle. It doesn't care what you put in there, it's going to crush it and then slice it. We will not discuss the things that a high-school kid will put in a large hydraulic smashing/slicing machine, but I will admit to being the reason that by the end of my first year there, the blade was about as sharp as the head of my dick and required not just sharpening but outright replacement.

It's quite simple to operate, you only have two buttons and a foot pedal. Put the paper in the right place on the table, noting the yellow strip of plastic set in the table where the blade will come down. Push the pedal with your foot and the hydraulic clamp comes down to hold the paper in place. Note that you often need to have your hands very close to this, and it doesn't give a fuck if your hand is in the way when it comes down. Many people have learned what a "degloving" injury is this way.

Assuming you did your job with half a brain and were paying attention, you then put your two healthy and intact hands along the front edge of the machine about 3 feet apart and then push the two big buttons at the same time. Only then will the four-foot-long razor blade come down and shear off anything from a single page up to a couple of reams in one smooth slice.

I've done this so many times that I've actually done it in my dreams. It's easy, relaxing... mind-numbing. I've spent hours in front of this machine and completed many thousands of cuts.

When you're standing in front of the cutter, about two feet directly behind you is a medium-sized Gestetner offset press, somewhere in a 200 or 300 series. The gentleman who was running it that day was a gigantic, dopey kid with platinum blonde hair and skin so pale he was teetering on Albinism. He carried the physique of a pudgy gorilla and had an IQ roughly approaching room temperature on his best days. He was about six-and-a-half feet tall and had forearms as thick as my thighs. At that moment, he had a rag in one hand and the jog button under his other.

That was the moment when every person reading this who has ever been a pressman at any point in history, just visibly twitched and gave an understanding wince.

An offset printing press is fundamentally two massive

slabs of steel set on edge with as many rollers as some little German man can figure out how to set between them. There are rollers for water, ink, plates, blankets, and they come in every form you can imagine: knurled steel, shiny chrome, hard rubber, and even cloth. Offset printing is all about the rollers.

All of these rollers are set in motion by only a few controls. There's the typical Go and Stop buttons, the Big Red E-Stop on every press, and there's a forward and reverse Jog button. "Jog" means to move the machine just a small amount, and it inches everything around just a little bit and at a slow speed for as long as you push the button. It's a common cleaning practice to jog the machine just a fraction of a turn, wipe everything you can see, jog a little more, wipe some more, over and over again.

What you absolutely fucking do not ever do is move any part of the machine while your hand is near it. Because the rollers are almost all in contact with the roller next to them, and wherever two rollers meet is called a "pinch point". The space between them is just enough to fit a thin film of ink, water, or a sheet of paper. Because the ends of the rollers are set in bearings pressed into giant slabs of steel, they don't stretch worth a shit. Running anything through these gaps aside from the ink, water, and paper that they were designed for results in a level of excitement, expensive sounds, and injuries that no pressman ever wishes to experience. Any press will handily remove body parts, and large ones have eaten men whole in what can only be described as a horrific and gruesome way to die.

Modern presses are festooned with guards and even contact rails for the larger pinch points. The contact rails will emergency-stop the machine if you bump into one, and will usually save your life, but not your arm.

None of that, however, was on the mind of the idiot albino gorilla who was cleaning that press at that moment, though. Running a printing press is only about ten percent of your time as a pressman. These presses will blast five thousand sheets of paper through in an hour with ease. The actual printing is done before you know it. In reality, you spend about ten percent of your time running the job, about twenty percent setting the machine up, and about a thousand percent of your time cleaning the damn press. This is not a career where people wear nice clothes.

The high albedo, albino, gorilla was on this third color of the day, cleaning the Cyan from his press as I was cutting the sheets of business cards for the school faculty into neat little stacks. This had been going on for the better part of half an hour when I heard a quiet, little voice muddled in the din like a fart in a hurricane.

"Uhhhhhhh... Borz?" the gorilla said, at a level that would have been appropriate for a conversation in an elevator.

He never yelled. He never raised his voice, even once. He didn't flail or throw things. He was perfectly calm. If he was any more laid back, he'd have been in a coma. What he did do was get even paler. His face looked like a sheet of 110 Index.

"Uhhhhhhhhh... (the sound of a human brain trying to find second gear)... Borz?" he said, several more times before it registered in my own brain, and I turned around. People shouting, "Hey Borz!" was a common thing in that room, and as he'd said it so quietly, it didn't really register my attention. Besides, I was focused on my own low-forgiveness task.

And that's when I turned around behind me and saw the damn fool with his middle finger about an inch farther into the pinch-point between the two ink rollers on top of the machine than anything thicker than a film of ink can fit. That had to hurt enough to make The Pope say motherfucker.

"Aw, fuck! **BORZ!!**" I shouted at the top of my lungs while taking two steps and punching the nearest Big Red Emergency Button on the wall. There were a couple of these in the room, and they were the emergency shutoff for every circuit feeding the presses. It was the button that turned off the world and was on top of the list of things you *do not fuck with*. The roar of the room stopped in an instant; you could have heard a mouse pissing on a cotton ball.

Thirty people all stopped whatever they were doing, yanked into a new reality by the sudden silence, and heads started prairie-dogging above equipment and the cubicle-height dividing wall near the prepress area. I looked up and the first thing I could see was Borz on a dead run from across the room. He lept clear over a waist-high Itek press like it was a thousand-pound hurdle; three long strides later he had slammed open the drawer in his desk. Within ten seconds of my pushing that button, he had a giant screwdriver in each hand and was running past me towards the dopey gorilla.

"Are you ok?" he asked, without stopping moving.

"Um, yeah," said the dipshit, still totally calm.

I stood back, only a couple of feet away, with a front-row seat as Borz marched up the Gestetner with poise, purpose, and passion. He threw his arms back, let loose a yell and with one smooth motion he brought his arms ferociously down and drove each of those screwdrivers deep into the gap of the offending rollers - missing the gorilla's finger by only an inch or two on either side. The gorilla nearly pissed himself. Christ, I nearly pissed myself, and I didn't even have any skin in this game.

And then came the moment of my young life that taught me a precious and permanent lesson about never judging an individual by their outward appearances alone.

Borz gave a loud grunt, set his shoulders into it, and heaved with one arm while pulling with the other. He began applying a staggering amount of force into the screwdrivers, so much so that the hardened shafts began to noticeably bend. Forthwith, his upper shirtsleeves stretched, bulged, and went as tight as a funeral drum. In a matter of seconds, with a growl from him and the creaking and popping sounds of permanent damage promising a lengthy repair bill from the ink system, he hate-fucked that press to a crygasm and levered up a gap between the rollers big enough that I could have fit my hand through it.

The gap opened up leaving the kid's smashed fingertip smeared against one of the rollers for a moment until he quickly pulled back his hand and the fingertip peeled off with it, dangling in space unnaturally, as thin as a piece of cardstock. By now, a crowd had circled to witness the spectacle and the sight of the finger was too much for one of the guys in the back. He narrowly made it into the hall before loudly making the second biohazard from our classroom that day.

Moments later, the gorilla was in a car being driven to the emergency room of the hospital in town.

We all stood there in shock at what we had just seen - **did nerdy little Borz just fucking *DO* that?**

What none of us knew was that the man who we had only known as the nerdy guy with the big glasses and the walrus 'stache, was actually a championship windsurfer in his summers off and spent his time carving waves from Michigan to Maui. When he wasn't surfing, he was building race cars and doing things with Mazda's that God and Wankel never intended. Under that short-sleeved, button-down, engineering outfit, was a set of arms with muscles that could snap your bitch ass in half.

Borz was a secret badass hiding the ripped body of a surfer dude with a layer of nerd camouflage; he lived the quiet life of a tradesman and educator in the backwoods of rural Michigan.

The world slowly came back into gear after we all spent a good ten minutes just taking in all that had happened. I went back to cutting my cards and just being quietly in awe of the impressive feat I'd just witnessed, with a fair bit of newfound respect for Borz.

The gorilla came back the next day with a big bandage and splint on his finger, he was fine in the end, but his middle finger is a half-inch shorter to this day. For the remainder of his time in High School, he was given the new nickname, "Lefty".

Heroes are quietly lurking everywhere; never underestimate the nerds. Some of them are pretty fuckin' rockstar.

Thank you Borz, you're still "BAAAAD!" Even now, twenty-seven years later and a decade after your retirement, you're still one of my heroes. Thank you for your patience, your persistence, and for never giving up on me, or the countless other dumbass problem kids whose lives you helped shape. I am unendingly thankful for the lessons you instilled in me, not just in knowing my points and my picas, but knowing craftsmanship, dedication, and treating people with decency and respect. You made a hell of a difference in a thousand lives, and I'm proud to be just one example.

Thank you for being the greatest kind of hero.

8

THE WORST PHYSICAL PAIN I'VE EXPERIENCED

What's the worst physical pain you've ever experienced?

With a lifetime of making really stupid decisions and collecting scars, one would imagine that might be a difficult question for me. Anyone who has read the irrationally popular, embarrassing story of what is now my world-famous scar would be pretty sure they already know the answer - but they'd be wrong.

I've been shot in the shoulder by an angry girlfriend and stabbed and sliced by everything from a stupid friend with a hunting knife to a batshit crazy hobo with a boxcutter. A vengeful, stainless steel pipe clamp on a Magnetron pierced an artery and landed me in front of a hand surgeon so talented that he gave me eight stitches but took my girlfriend.

They've been married ten years now... *je ne regrette rien.*

I was blasted across the room from a failed high voltage capacitor that went off like a grenade and lost five pounds I couldn't afford to be poisoned by a woman who didn't believe in modern medicine. I've been tossed out of a moving Honda onto a brick-paved street in the ghetto and fallen two stories down a shaftway to land on top of the elevator.

I've heard my right knee sound like celery as it bent ninety degrees in the wrong direction when I was plowed over by a small private airplane rolling down a hill. I've been hit-n-run by a drunk driver, sucker-punched by a large model airplane, and pulverized my distal phalanges so hard I had a prosthetic plastic toenail for a year. I've had my septum crushed by powerful magnets and gotten a Five Finger Death Punch eyeful of high-octane menthol oil.

I was twenty-eight when I crossed the line of having my 100th suture, by thirty I had broken my nose seven times. To this day you can still see the faint blue plastic tip of the bottle rocket embedded in the front of my forehead, and on the other side, you can still feel the dent from the steel corner of a speaker cabinet.

If you look down the centerline of my face you can see that the midline of my eyes, the root, dorsum, and tip of my nose, my philtrum, and the space between my two front teeth are all in complete disagreement with no three points sharing a common line.

I've had teeth knocked down my throat by an angry brother, had my jaw broken by a mountain when I took a forty-foot whip and given myself a root canal with a Dremel and the rearview mirror of my 1986 Chevy S-10. I've put my dentist's kid through college and worn dentures since my twenties.

I ain't pretty, but I've got some great stories.

I've swallowed more blood than beer.

But nothing, fucking nothing, compared to catching a six-foot-long, roughly half-million-volt electrical arc to the nose.

That hurt.

Clearly, I've made some bad decisions. I shall tell you the story...

Back in my younger, dumber, college days, I was screwing around with some friends in the garage with one of my Tesla Coils. It was a beautiful summer day, we had the door open, and were setting up to do a few runs in the driveway at high power. We could only run this system at very low levels in the garage because it was simply too big to operate inside anything smaller than a gymnasium. At full power it created a writhing, screaming, ten-foot arc that would spall pocks in wet concrete and kill anything it caught.

This was rather early in my HV career, and it was a crude system by current standards. A Tesla Coil is actually a very simple machine that works like an electrical swingset. If you apply a small pulse of energy from one tuned circuit at just the right time into another tuned circuit, you can cause it to resonate and get a very high voltage output. The end result is that you get lightning out the top.

Think of it like pushing someone on a swing in a park. If you hit them with a baseball bat they won't actually move very far at all. But if you give them a little push with two fingers, at just the right time, over and over again you can eventually get them high enough that the screaming starts.

Things like this are why physics memes involving kids on swings are a thing. It's what happens when you spend too much time on your infinite frictionless plane with nothing to keep you company but spherical cows.

I was working with Andrew, my roommate at the time. He was a good guy but wouldn't make a pimple on an engineer's ass; he believed electricity was simply commercialized magic. But he was capable enough to be my second set of hands while we slowly brought the primary tank system into tune. This is a deeply boring process that takes a while on a large system and is marked by long periods of tedious precision movements interspersed with moments of hustle and the twiddling of connections.

At least, as boring as you can get when you're throwing lightning around the driveway.

Tesla Coils are fussy bitches. They're deceptively simple - you can scrawl the entire circuit schematic on a napkin in less than a minute in a vain attempt to impress a girl with your elite physicist brain - but to get one to actually work well is an exercise in patience and persistence.

Therein lies the problem.

If it's not in tune, it simply sucks huge amounts of power from the wall and doesn't actually do anything but make a lot of noise, welder-flash UV light, and inflate your power bill. However, when it's tuned right, the noise changes, it sings, and you're hurling the elemental forces of a God around at your command.

It's better than sex.

To get it all in final tune, all you have to do is have a little clamp clipped to the right spot on a coil of copper tubing. That's it, it's super simple.

However, that spot can be only an inch or so wide on a

fifty-foot-long coil of tubing. Oh, and you can't touch it, because it's operating at 20,000 volts and will easily kill you the moment you don't respect it. For comparison, your wall socket (in the US) is only 120 volts.

So, you put the clip in place, turn on the power, see if it's making an output at all (which means you're getting close), note how long the output arc is, turn it off, ground the system out for safety so it doesn't bite your ass from the stored charge, move the clamp a little, pull the safety off and try all over again. All in all, it's not a difficult process and only takes about 30 seconds...

Now, do that fifty times.

Andrew got bored.

Andrew is also a bit of a cunt who doesn't truly appreciate the gravity of fucking around with the finger of God.

Showcasing his ignorance, Andrew thought he'd be funny and blipped the power button for just a second.

I was standing about six or eight feet away from the machine, having just made my 40th or so adjustment to the primary tap when I heard it spin up and stupidly turned to look at the object of my terror.

The arc sought its path of least resistance to the lanky meatbag filled with electrolytes and found it on the top of my nose.

The rotary spark gap was delivering 360 pulses per second into the primary system at that moment, and I got blasted for about a second before Andrew's brain processed my soul-piercing scream and realized what had happened.

In the worlds of physics, fear, and pain, a second is a fuck of a long time. Hold your breath for a second, easy... but try stopping a chainsaw in your asscheeks for a second, because that's about how bad it hurt.

I was shocked roughly 360 times at, give or take, a half-million volts. The contact point was my nose, and as the lightning ran through my body searching for ground, it went out my big toe setting my shoe to smoldering and smoking in the process.

Now, the classic 1-10 pain scale used by the medical profession works like this:

One: Very minor annoyance - occasional minor twinges
Two: Minor annoyance - occasional
Three: Annoying enough to be distracting
Four: Can be ignored if you are really involved in your work but still distracting.
Five: Can't be ignored for more than 30 minutes.
Six: Can't be ignored for any length of time, but you can still go to work and participate in social activities with some effort.
Seven: Makes it difficult to concentrate, interferes with sleep, but you can still function semi-normally with a large effort.
Eight: Physical activity is severely limited. You can read and converse with effort. Nausea and dizziness may occur.
Nine: Unable to speak, crying out, or moaning uncontrollably - pain may make you pass out.
Ten: Unconscious. Pain makes you pass out.

So, three is a deep bruise, five is a toothache, and eight is breaking your arm... you get the idea.

A ten is often described as simply "abject terror". It's not even a conscious thing. Hit a ten and you're just completely, instantly fucked up beyond functioning.

This was a ten. There was no conscious thought at all. My reptile brain just took over, and all I could do was scream at the top of my lungs and piss down my leg. Once the power stopped, I simply collapsed. It was very similar to when you see someone get tazed - just with about ten times the voltage and worlds more energy behind it. Tasers run off a nine-volt battery, this Tesla Coil draws as much power as your entire house.

I remained mostly conscious, but I had to just lay there on the gravel and make seal noises for a minute while my brain went through POST.

I hurt in places you don't even know you own, and it took a few days for my brain to fire on all cylinders again.

Andrew never touched a piece of my equipment again, and he moved out only a couple of weeks later. I will never know if the reason for his departure was the guilt over nearly electrocuting me or if it was the fact that his girlfriend heard the whole story while I was recovering and decided to make me feel better in any way she could.

Turns out, she could. I enacted my revenge by banging her like an old screen door as loudly and frequently as possible. They broke up, he moved out, and she and I ended up dating for over a year and a half until she graduated and moved back home.

I regret nothing.

9

DICK PHYSICS AND THE MOUSE TRAP

"Any sufficiently advanced technology is indistinguishable from magic."
-    Arthur C. Clarke's Third Law

Gird thy loins, this one's going to sting. But like most painful lessons, you're going to learn something interesting.

Most people don't have a terribly good understanding of pressure. If you were about to have something parked on your foot, would you rather it be an M1 Abrams Tank, a burly guy on a mountain bike, or a petite little woman wearing high-heeled shoes?

This is a pretty obvious choice it seems, but nature is a mother and physics often isn't intuitive.

Choose the tank. It's only pushing down at 15 psi (pounds per square inch). This means that for every square inch of area that the tank is actually touching the ground, there are fifteen pounds of force. It would feel about the same as putting a large bag of dog food, balanced on its corner, on your foot. Not comfortable, but once it moves, you'll be fine.

Our gentleman on the mountain bike? He's got about 40 pounds per square inch of ground pressure because his contact area is much smaller than the tank. With only a couple of inches to hold him up, those inches need to do a lot more work than they did for the tank. This one is going to hurt, but you'll probably be ok.

The woman, as if often the case, is going to be the one that leaves you scarred. That stiletto heel is coming down with a bone-crushing force of over 450 pounds per square inch. Even though she has the smallest amount of weight overall, it is spread out over a very tiny area.

Thus, it is better to be run over by a tank than crushed under a woman's heel.

The world of Physics is filled with non-obvious demonstrations of scientific oddities when you start playing around with pressure and the dark arts of Fluid Dynamics.

And that's how I ended up with a mousetrap on my dick in front of a hundred people.

Ok, ok, just breathe. I get it, this bears a little explaining. Get comfortable, we're going on a bit of a ride...

It has been written that Philosophy is the search for Truth and Understanding, but I have doubts. They've been at it for thousands of years and still can't even agree amongst themselves. Philosophy is artistic psychotherapy and furious concerted cognitive masturbation for geniuses that have had too much to think.

If you want to find the Truth of the universe, it will be down the quiet pathway of Mathematics. It's what Politics dreams of, being the only place where you'll ever find simple solutions to complicated problems. It's the only place where any black and white absolute truths exist. Mathematics is what reveals Cosmos from Chaos. Math is the language of nature, and the Universe itself. It's the entire foundation upon which we rest Physics.

And Physics is everything. It's the bridge between the Cerebral and the Tangible, the world of numbers, and the world of matter. Physics is the dream that stuff is made of.

Physics is the study of Energy, the ability to do work, and the ability to cause disruption, motion, and change.

I've been studying Physics since I first stuck a table knife into a wall outlet. My first lesson was that people can be pretty damn stupid.

One of the great downsides to having spent my life as a science teacher and magician is having developed a profound understanding of how easily people can be outright amazed by the simplest of easily explained natural phenomena, especially if you just spend a little time on preparation and presentation. This is why there's a whole genre of basic-bitch housewives that are enthralled by the sublimation of solidified carbon dioxide when you drop some in a punchbowl for Halloween.

I can't count how many times I've seen that one on television. I die a little inside every time they pass that off as some amazing and advanced thing. We won't talk about how they're standing ten feet from a device that can miraculously turn light particles into organized packets of electrical transmissions. We won't talk about how they're wearing a device full of miniaturized surface-mount technology that is capturing their voice in a pair of 16-digit numbers 44,100 times a second with circuits so tiny that they're manufactured with beams of fucking light! No, it's dry ice… that's their idea of a miracle of science and technology.

My sainted Grandmother put the childproof outlet caps in every unused socket in the house to "keep the electricity from leaking out". This is despite the fact that my Grandfather, her husband, spent his entire adult life as a lineman building transmission towers for the electric company.

It's entirely possible that he told her to do it, in some form of epic 40-year-troll. God, I miss him.

We exist surrounded by an endless stream of unappreciated magic and miracles, founded in countless lifetimes of work in science and engineering, all being used by people who have no idea about how any of it actually works.

(sigh)

Fuckin' people.

Oh, that's right, let's talk about fucking people!

So, while you're sitting there with one hand on the keyboard watching midget furry porn, your twisted fucking brain triggers the timed release of neurotransmitters from the cavernous nerve terminals in your dick. This makes the smooth muscle fibers chill out for a bit and opens up the arterioles (which, as it turns out, is not actually a name for an obscure type of pasta) and arteries by increasing blood flow in not only the diastolic but the systolic phase as well.

The expanding sinusoids trap the incoming blood (well, most of it anyway).

EPICARICACY

Then your subtunical venular plexuses (between the tunica albuginea and the peripheral sinusoids) lock right the fuck down and reduce the venous outflow, a lot.

Your tight little tunica gets maxed to the nines, and that occludes the emissary veins in between the inside circular and outside linear layers, which binds up the venous outflow tighter than a Nun's nasty. At this point, there's barely any blood leaving your dick, and if it stays like this for too long parts of it will actually start to clot and you're in for a bad weekend with a BIG needle that hurts enough to make the pope say motherfucker.

By this point, the dissolved oxygen in your blood jumps up to about 1.74 psi and the intracavernous pressure in your dick climbs up to about 2 psi, and that gives you a substantial chub and makes you have to adjust your pants. Doctors would measure the pressure in your dick at about 100 mmHg because they don't use psi, they use Millimeters of Mercury because science, but that's about 2 psi.

By this point, you're off to the races. You find that perfect moment in the video when Bea Arthur slips into the bathtub filled with Tapioca and your brain responds by giving your ischiocavernosus muscles the highball signal, and you enter the "Rigid Erection Phase" as the pressures in your now throbbing cock jump again and can rise to several hundred millimeters of mercury.

It takes all of that, just for you to get a hard on.

Now two pounds per square inch may not sound like a whole lot but realize that's the same amount of pressure that the side of your house is getting if there's a 70 mile per hour storm raging. At 3 psi, most houses will collapse, and people start getting hurt. At 5 psi (that would be a 163

Mph wind) Most buildings collapse, injuries are universal, and fatalities are widespread. At only 10 psi, the pressure inside your garden tractor tire, reinforced concrete buildings are severely damaged or demolished and most people are killed. That's because 10 psi would be a 294 mile per hour storm. Nuclear bombs typically destroy cities with pressures in the 3-5 psi range.

So now you can tell people that your hardon has almost as much pressure as a city-shredding nuclear explosion.

So that's how this story came to be...

I was at a Kinky Christmas party at a friend's house with a hundred half-naked people who I didn't know, talking with a group of BDSM aficionados about the mechanism of the male erection. I was standing at the focus of a semicircle of drunken weirdos, perverts, and freaks (my kind of people) and asked if anyone wanted to see the most terrifying demonstration of science in the world.

The crowd cheered.

There's another kind of energy, that's not in any of the physics books and is far more dangerous than high voltage or the sudden release of compressed gasses. This is the energy of an enthusiastic crowd. The energy of a crowd can topple not only monuments but governments. It can send people across oceans to find new lands, and across space to explore new worlds. The energy of a cheering crowd is what allows people like Tom Mullica to do a stage show with forty lit cigarettes in his mouth. Yes, it's painful as hell, but you can just put that aside when there are hundreds of people screaming encouragement of your stupid behavior.

This is why you should always cheer when a runner passes

by. They need that more than you can imagine. They're feeding off your energy, you lazy bastard. So, help them along and give a yell.

I had the energy of a crowd, and my little semicircle of twenty people started to swell. I turned to my friend and loudly said,

"Find me a mousetrap!"

My horrible friend, the owner of the house appeared only a few seconds later from the kitchen and was holding a brand new two-pack of the classic wooden Victor mousetraps.

People started to look concerned.

"I'm going to need a nasty assistant," I said to a beautiful, freaky goth girl that I'd known for a decade. I unzipped my pants, she smiled, always a slut... for attention, and proceeded to help open up my arterioles as she sucked my smooth muscle.

The crowd cheered as we all enjoyed the fact that it had just become THAT kind of party.

I took off my hat and handed it off to my right, "pass it around and this show will have one hell of an ending," I said as I removed one of the mousetraps from its packaging.

It didn't take her long; I was empowered not only with the energy of a cheering crowd but also with a throbbing meat truncheon. Carefully, I placed the mousetrap on the dining room table beside me, pulled back the bail, and readied the trap.

The cheers turned into a cacophony of "wooooooooahhhhhh", "aw hell no!", and "oh shit". Everyone in the house was paying attention now, even the music had stopped. I found this impressive given that a large number of the people here held a strong appreciation for the creative application of pain.

I reached down and gently tugged her ponytail, "I need that back please," I said. In one smooth movement, as the crowd went so quiet you could have heard a mouse pissing on a cotton ball, I pulled my dick from her mouth, spun on my heel ninety degrees to my left, and holding it at the base smacked it down on the table with the last three inches landing squarely in the mousetrap. The mousetrap triggered and snapped down on my dick.

The only time I've ever seen a reaction like that was when some sneaky bastard thought it would be a good idea to show "The Crying Game" for the campus movie night. The crowd completely lost its shit. One guy right in front passed out cold and folded up like a week's dirty laundry on the floor, another gentleman started running across the furniture screaming like it was his dick in the mousetrap, and everyone was cheering and screaming.

Quickly, I lifted my dick off the table and spun around back to face the crowd head-on, held my dick up for just a moment with the mousetrap rattling on the end, and then pulled open the trap and freed my manhood. The entire stunt lasted perhaps five seconds. The cheers and screams went on for at least thirty.

I took a bow, and when my hat came back around it had more cash in it than I typically made in a month. Merry Christmas to me and my dick, from Physics Santa.

I was unscathed and unscarred (except for the big one on

the bottom of my dick, but that's another story) because I had faith in Physics. Over the years I would go on to do "The Mousetrap Trick" a few more times, enough that it became a bit of a legend among the weirdo crowd of freaks and perverts that I have had the sincere honor to hang out with. They've asked me to write the whole story behind it a thousand times, so now I've finally gotten around to doing just that. I hope you enjoyed it. :)

Yes, doing the stunt hurts, but it's not the instant catastrophic damage that everyone imagines it to be. The "trick" behind it is simple: liquids don't compress. The physics behind your hard on is the exact same as the process behind how an average man can lift an entire car with a small hydraulic jack. It's what lets a tiny electric motor lift an elevator full of people and what lets a rider stop a thousand pounds of motorcycle moving at a hundred miles an hour with only two fingers.

Now, try that with a limp dick and you'll be damaged for life if you're lucky enough to not instantly lose a few inches. But if you have the raging erection of a Brahman bull, the iron shaft, or the honeymoon hard on of a young man in his twenties fueled by the energy of a screaming crowd... well with a lever like that and a blonde to brace it against, you can move the world.

.

.

10

THE GOODENOW SPHERE

I don't know what the hell I was thinking, but it seemed like a good idea at I've silently shouldered this secret for decades. As promised, I have patiently waited for the last of the three men in charge to die before I shared it. I kept my side of the bargain, and after all these years, thanks to a combination of the frailty that comes with old age and a virus that comes from an undercooked bat, I can tell the world. Up until this point, only half a dozen people have ever known anything about this.

This is not a happy story. That's not the point. This isn't some sexy secret. This is a bundle of quite possibly unsolvable questions that will leave you with nothing but an itch in your brain that you'll never be able to scratch. This secret is an odd bit of small-town history that has plagued the minds of every man that's known of it for nearly thirty years. My only slim hope in ever solving this mystery is to share it. Perhaps you, gentle reader, may be the one to finally solve this puzzle.

But I sincerely doubt it.

This story is going to piss you off and leave you uncomfortable, unfulfilled, and rife with questions. I feel the exact same way about this experience, and I lived it.

That's how life is sometimes, you don't always get everything wrapped up nice and tidy at the end of the episode.

I can tell you the small part of this that I experienced, but I'm not going to give you a wild hypothesis or conjecture because I simply don't have any answers. I believe it's better to give you the truth of the experience than just blowing smoke up your ass to make you feel better. At least we get to have company and commiseration in our cooperative confusion.

What I will give you is the simple facts as I saw them myself, as a first-hand witness and actual member of the small crew that cleaned up the mess. Beyond that, all of the rest is left as an exercise to you, gentle reader. I offer no explanation, no solid conclusion, and no resolution.

What you choose to do with this information, is up to you. I seek no reward or gain from any of this. I refuse to deal with any press or give interviews on it. I have nothing else to offer. Everything I know of the matter is included here. You're entirely on your own. Don't bother asking me any questions. I have no answers. That's the problem.

Located a town over from where I grew up is a little place called Marne, Michigan. It's a dot on a map with the claim to fame being that it hosts the Berlin Raceway, home of weekly formula car races and the annual local fair. Aside from the fair every year, nothing much happens there. It's so small that the town's only highway exit doesn't even have a gas station anymore. A tiny place in the shadow of Grand Rapids. If you ever happen to stop by, get a grilled cheese sandwich at the Interurban Cafe (the old train station). They're the best I've ever had.

For me, and a small team of other people, Marne holds a

secret that none of us have ever understood. It's not in any history books, and the official account is that none of this ever happened.

Now, I've spent a lifetime leaving footprints in places I never stepped, having conversations that never happened, and working on projects that never existed. They pay well and promptly. So long as the paycheck is good, I'll sign your NDA, work on your project team, and keep your secrets for as long as you ask. Such is the nature of my career - doing prototypical engineering and fabrication all the way from the world of high-energy physics to improving manufacturing processes, to making custom sex machines. An engineer's whole life is filled with other people's secrets.

If you take a short walk from the main road to the back of the cemetery the scar on the Earth is still there, but you'd never guess what it came from. This is the story of the Goodenow Sphere.

One early morning in August of 1994 I got a phone call and was told to get my ass over to the cemetery, immediately. Fifteen minutes later I pulled up to find a county sheriff's car blocking the entrance. After getting my name, he let me pass and instructed me to drive around through another entrance. I drove all the way to the back of the cemetery to find my boss with his excavator sitting on the trailer behind his old truck.

He was talking with three men I didn't know. Two men were wearing suits, and one looked like a farmer. They all took a look at me as I quietly wandered up and stood behind my boss, but nobody stopped talking. I just listened and studied the scene feeling a bit of an adrenaline rush from breathing air above my pay grade. I had the feeling my boss felt the same way, but he faked it well.

Nobody said anything about it, but we both had that feeling of visiting someone else's church. This just wasn't our place, and we didn't belong here.

They were standing next to a trench that looked like a long, wedge-shaped gouge in the back of the cemetery. At the bottom of the hole, was a smooth, grey, stone sphere about a yard in diameter. At first, I thought it was a meteorite.

It turns out this was the most terra of terrestrial origins - it was a tombstone. Well, the top of a tombstone to be exact. Everyone knew exactly what it was and where it came from because it had been sitting at the front of the cemetery for generations right on top of the Goodenow family monument. The only thing more conspicuous than its absence from the plinth it had rested on since long before I was born, was the fucking huge hole in the ground leading up to where it was now resting at the other end of the unpaved two-track to the back of the cemetery.

It was almost three hundred feet - a full football field - from the center of the plinth cup that it had originally sat on to the top of the sphere where we found it, forcefully embedded in the ground. It had crossed over two of the roads in the cemetery and was just to the southwest of the farthest intersection back from the center entrance. This giant, stone sphere was resting about two feet underground with dirt smooshed up and around the back of it in such a way that it was very obvious it had landed there with immense force. The trajectory was obvious from the long crater carved in the ground that started near the intersection of the cemetery two-tracks and ended where the stone sat, half-buried in the earth.

The crater was a thirty-foot scar that started only a few inches from the cemetery road. The sod at the beginning looked torn, but the dirt underneath had smooth edges and was clearly made by the sphere as it landed. It was as if a marble was loaded into a slingshot and released at a 5-degree angle from the ground - except this marble was four feet in diameter. This was a large, smooth stone weighing several thousand pounds.

We all stood around, smoking cigarettes and mumbling, bewildered with only one question on our minds - how the hell did it get there?

Initially, we thought it was some kind of prank, maybe a few bored farm kids doing stupid shit. Vandalism was the most obvious explanation. This kind of thing happens in cemeteries from time to time, when asshole kids will kick over a headstone or something. It doesn't happen out in the country much though, that's more of a city kid thing, but it does happen. Out here, the main reason you'll find kids in the cemetery at night is either to smoke a joint or to look for a quiet place to get laid.

But how the hell would they have moved over 2500lbs of granite nearly three hundred feet, in one night, without leaving any tracks?

The sphere didn't look like it had been rolled across the cemetery, it would have left one hell of a mess in the grass and dirt if it had. The puzzle was, there were no markings or tracks on the ground at all. Not near the original location, or where it was resting now (except for the giant, sloping crater, of course). There were no tire tracks, no heavy equipment treads, and not even any shoe prints.

There was no evidence of anyone having been there recently, except us.

And yet, somehow it landed here. It looked like it had

been picked up and tossed at a shallow angle. Imagine pushing a marble into modeling clay, it looked like that. No dirt had been removed, just pushed out of the way as it landed.

We spent the morning digging it out gently. We had to remove all of the dirt around the sphere with the excavator, and then change over to the larger bucket and move the excavator to a closer position so we could gently scoop it up out of the hole.

Once we had it out, the suits wanted to give it an inspection. I originally thought it was to make certain it hadn't been damaged, but the exact reason was never told to me. I never asked, but it's an aspect of this whole experience that's always bugged me a little bit.

We went to eat lunch and pick up the Bobcat while the suits stood looking at the sphere. When we got back, they seemed satisfied with their inspection. We began several hours of precarious fiddling to get the massive sphere across the cemetery and gently balanced back upon its plinth. Mind you we had to do all of this without damaging up any of the other graves, headstones, or tearing the grass completely to hell, but we managed it without incident. We cleaned up all the dirt and debris around the monument so if you didn't know, you couldn't tell.

After we got it back in place, my boss used the excavator's blade and I drove the Bobcat to repair and smooth the impact crater in the back of the cemetery. We never did get it quite right, but it would pass a casual glance. We never added any new dirt, so it settled a bit and left a shallow depression in the grass. Even now, decades later, if you walk out to the spot you can see that something big happened there long ago. Despite being an active cemetery, this back section where the stone sphere crashed still does not have any gravestones. For the curious, the remains of the cater are on the West side of the entrance road at the far back, just South of the little drive that runs sideways, dividing the new section from the old.

In the process of fixing the crater, we tore the hell out of the lawn and left a massive amount of caterpillar tracks everywhere, even on the hard-packed dirt of the driveway and cemetery roads. There is simply no way that someone came in with large machinery to move that in the middle of the night - there would have been tracks everywhere.

As I write this, twenty-five years later, the sphere remains where it's always sat, silently standing vigil as a notable local landmark just inside the center entrance to the Marne cemetery. I have no idea who the Goodenow family was, but I like to think they enjoyed the show and the ruckus that went into putting their monument back in its rightful home.

As far as how the stone got to where we found it, or any events of the night before, I have nothing but questions. A lifetime of engineering, building, design, and moving heavy shit has empowered me with the incredible opportunity to learn a million lessons; but I've never figured out the mystery of the Goodenow Sphere.

.

11

THE RACOON CANNON

I can tell this story now, the statute of limitations has long since passed.

I have never achieved the hallmark of genius that is "building a better mousetrap", but I did once cross the milestone of redneck engineering badassery that is building a High Voltage Raccoon Cannon.

See, we had a raccoon problem in the garage. I was living in the student ghetto at the time and situated right in the middle of a whole neighborhood that hosted gigantic parties on a nearly constant basis. Parties brought crowds, who brought food, who left trash, and attracted all manner of wildlife. Now that on its own isn't much of a problem. If they just came, ate, and left we'd have gotten along just fine.

But it's not that the bastards just ate things, they processed them too, and the world was their toilet. Apparently, my garage was the most fabulous toilet in town for the dozens of Raccoons that roamed about.

I was not ok with this. I used part of the garage as a workshop, and the smell was horrendous.

I tried calling the city, and the woman I talked to actually laughed at me. They're happy to come clean up a dead one in the road, but if it's got a heartbeat, it's not their problem. She tried to feed me a line about how it's "God's plan" and was not appreciative when I told her that God's plan needs some revisions because it's got several obvious flaws.

I tried calling a pest control specialist; he was already very familiar with my neighborhood. He told me he'd be happy to come bag a bunch of them, but it would cost a ton that we both knew I didn't have, and they would just keep coming back. He was a cool guy, and I appreciated his honesty.

I knew I had to come up with something better. I got creative.

My initial plan was to zap the bastards (I worked in high-voltage, high-energy engineering), so I started thinking down that path. Plan A was to make a plate, perhaps two feet square, ground it, and hang a live, hot wire over it with bait. But that would have just left me with a daily dead critter to dispose of. I needed something cleaner and more elegant. Bonus points if it got rid of them in a way they didn't come back and was self-resetting.

I got to work.

After some thought, I decided on a cannon. The idea was very simple. Mount the tube on an angle that could be adjusted for where I wanted the flaming wad of meat and fur to land. Put a can of tuna in the bottom as bait. Apply a high amount of energy across the trigger bolts, and just wait for a curious creature to close the spark gap with its head. The blast from the arc/boiling head would kill the critter and send it out the open end of the pipe, likely at a high velocity.

I cut a piece of 6", solid-core, heavy-walled PVC pipe to about three feet long and solvent-welded a cap on one end. I drilled 6 holes in the side and installed some ¼-20 carriage bolts with the heads on the inside of the pipe. Four of the holes were for mounting the pipe on a wide, adjustable stand made from some scraps of Unistrut. The other two holes, down near the cap, were the trigger for the cannon.

Simple, clean, efficient.

It took me only an afternoon to make the cannon, stand, and power supply. The energy was stored in a massive, 400-pound pulse capacitor rated for about 10,000 Joules at 50 kV. It was charged from a simple, low-current supply that traded cheap and easy for a very low cycle rate and just held the capacitor at a float charge. The whole contraption was ungodly dangerous and could have easily killed anyone who went into the garage and started messing with it. So, for safety, I simply removed one of the windows in the garage door and slid the cannon to a position where it would shoot the ball of fur and meat through the 12" x 24" hole that remained.

It was art.

I gave everything a final check, dropped an open can of tuna down the tube, made sure it was well clear of the electrodes, plugged in the power supply, and went to bed.

Now, no plan is perfect. But clearly, there were some parts of this that I had not given sufficient thought to. Chief among them was the sound.

Holy FUCK it was loud.

Somewhere in the small hours, the house shook, and the windows rattled with a single WHOOOOMP! My roommates, my neighbors, and I went from dreaming to screaming in an instant. My bedroom was on the back of the house, about six feet from the garage and maybe ten feet from the cannon. It sounded like someone had set off a bomb in my bedroom.

Now vibrating between fight-or-flight with adrenaline, I got up, got dressed, and went outside. Several of my neighbors were already there.

They did not appreciate my exceptional engineering and genius problem-solving abilities. I immediately unplugged the machine. We had a little chat about being considerate of other people's need for sleep, the perils of living next door to a weirdo engineer, had a smoke and a good laugh about it all, and everyone went back to bed as friends.

(Our own, individual beds, we were not THAT kind of friends, and this isn't one of those kinds of stories. But check out my other writings.)

In the morning, after sleeping for an extra hour, I ate breakfast and wandered outside. I wanted to see the results of the one successful firing of the 'Coon Cannon.

The tube itself was fine. The tuna can was still in the bottom, the mount had moved almost imperceptibly from the recoil. I thought to myself, "Next time, use concrete anchors". I walked to the end of the driveway looking for the remains.

However, they weren't there. I looked all over and couldn't find anything left. I smiled at the success and imagined the flaming mist that must have shot out of the tube to be dispersed without a trace as I lit my morning cigarette and enjoyed the cool morning air of what would be a beautiful summer's day.

About halfway through my cigarette, I happened to look up, and I started laughing so hard that the neighbor girl came out to see what the hell was going on.

My house was the third one up the street on the end of a shared driveway between us, and two other houses. My garage terminated the driveway, and it was a clear, open, straight line from the front of my garage all the way to the curb.

Across the street was a large dormitory for the overpriced, liberal-arts college that flanked one edge of our entire neighborhood. A beautiful brick structure was several stories high with pretty rock walls and manicured grounds.

About fifty feet up the side, smashed into the antique brick facade, was thirty pounds of burnt, ground raccoonbuger. It looked like a furry tumor on the side of the pretentious building.

We both laughed until we couldn't breathe.

The cannon never fired again. I dismantled it, trashed the pipe, and the capacitor went on to become parts of future projects over the years.

But it worked. I had a novel idea, tested it, and proved it. That was enough for me.

The dorm's furry tumor remained there for weeks. I don't know if it simply went unnoticed, or if nobody could figure out how the hell to get it down. But I checked every morning and after a few weeks, it simply fell off the wall and landed in a shrub. A day later, it was gone altogether. I was smart enough to never inquire about it, but I can only imagine the questions in the poor landscaper's mind when he discovered it.

I learned to accept the Raccoons, and to be fair they weren't the worst neighbors I've ever had to deal with.

But that's another story altogether...

12

THE EXPLODING JAPANESE HEATER

It really is a miracle that I've lived this long.

In the winter of 1994, I was living with a couple dozen of my weirdo friends in a not-quite-abandoned and not-yet-condemned warehouse at 344 Ionia Southwest, in downtown Grand Rapids, Michigan. We were soul-crushingly poor and despite that, we were having the time of our lives. At any given moment we could afford water, heat, and electricity... pick any two.

It was January, and that month it was the heat that had lost the budgetary battle. We simply had to use so much gas to heat the monstrosity of the building we lived in, that we couldn't afford to have it on. The cold settled in so hard that the paint was peeling off the brick walls. We bundled and huddled, not just to stay warm, but to stay alive.

Kent, an old high school teacher of mine who would become a lifelong friend (and whom I would personally nominate for sainthood), gave me an incredible gift that Christmas. It was a cantankerous, '80s vintage, kerosene heater. That damn thing would both save my life and nearly kill me a few hundred times over the course of the winter.

The heater was a boring, beige box with a glass cylinder in the center behind a large stainless reflector. It had two hatches on top, one on the left that opened to reveal a removable stainless fuel tank that held about a gallon of kerosene, and one in the center that opened down into the burner, its glass chimney, coils, and wick. It had a single big control knob and various buttons and levers near the bottom of the front panel. I'm sure it was a simple machine to operate if you knew what you were doing, but all of the labels and instructions were in Japanese.

Some people can speak many languages, they call these people Polyglots. Some people can speak two, they call them bilingual. However, a great many people can speak only one language, they call these people Americans. I fall into that third category.

The primary danger I faced was from carbon monoxide poisoning, I knew that much. So, my first priority was to ensure that I had a decent chimney outside and adequate ventilation. I had already spent a month worried about dying in my sleep from hypothermia; I didn't want to go out from CO in a similar style.

It was quick work to knock out a single pane from one of the towering windows in my apartment and replace it with a small piece of sheet metal. I ran a crude chimney from the back of the heater out through the window and set to work filling the tank and trying to figure out how in the hell to make the damn thing work.

The first thing to do was to begin a detailed and methodical exploration of each button. This was "black box" engineering, and I figured I'd work through it step-by-step. In proper terms, I was just screwing around with the buttons hoping something would start making heat.

There was some manner of cocking mechanism involved with one of the buttons and the knob. I never did really figure out just how the hell this worked. But after the first fifteen minutes of swearing at it, I had deduced that the cocking mechanism had something to do with the fuel shutoff. I could tell because if you cocked it the room started to smell like kerosene, and if you tripped it, and it went THUNK, the fire immediately went out.

There was a little finger that would raise up and touch the wick when you pressed down the lever. It took twenty seconds to figure out that this was some kind of electric hot-coil igniter and where to put the batteries. However, it took the next half an hour to find a stack of D-Cell batteries to make the damn thing work.

This was good because I'd been through easily a third of a big box of kitchen matches so far, with negligible luck, and had burned more matches than kerosene.

I kept playing with it, and I finally got it to light. I determined that you had to hold down the lever or it would just go out, but if you held it long enough, a spring-coil that went around the base of the wick got red hot. Once this sequence was complete, it would stay lit on its own so you could let go of the lever. Bam, fire!

Finally, IT WORKED!

I was radiantly thankful and sat basking in the warm glow from the tiny, little flame nestled down in the bottom of the glass tube. I just kind of zenned-out, feeling comfortable and happy for the first time in weeks. Everything was just wonderful... for about twenty minutes.

And then it twitched.

The fire seemed to have died, and a thick white fog began to fill the burner chamber and leak out down the front of the heater, clinging low to the concrete floor. The smell of kerosene filled my nostrils; I'd spent enough time playing with bonfires and grills to know that the fog was highly flammable, toxic, and altogether not something you really want to have inside. But the floor was concrete, the walls of the room were all brick, there was certainly nothing that could burn within ten feet of the heater, and I was desperately cold, so I took the chance.

I still backed well away from that infernal contraption, half certain I was going to need to get the garden hose out of my bathroom any moment.

For about thirty seconds the fog grew and spread, it floated about six inches from the front of the heater along the floor, then I heard a gurgle, a quiet hiss, and a frankly fucking terrifying *ssssSSHHWHUMP-Tink-CLANG!* as something reacted and the mixture got just right and ignited. A fireball shot out the top of the chimney, and the little hatch on top of the heater directly above the central flame popped up a few inches as fire spewed out and then slammed back down.

I nearly pissed myself and quickly learned that an excellent way to give yourself a serious head injury is to try and jump up and run while sitting cross-legged, wrapped in an old wool blanket on a concrete floor. Despite that, I was halfway across the room in seconds, screaming like a bitch as my knees and feet fought each other for who was going to get to the door first.

Afterward, though, it seemed fine. The stench went away, the fire came back, the bleeding on my forehead stopped, and Tojo's Revenge was making heat again. Still, I sat there and kept an eye on it. Slowly, over the next fifteen minutes, I cautiously inched my way back closer to the warmth.

And then, five minutes or so later, the whole cycle happened again. This time I was ready for it, but it still scared the living hell out of me. Any rational person would have tossed this thing in a dumpster, but I live in a place where the air hurts your face, and cold is one hell of a motivator.

I left it there and decided to come to peace with it. Cold can make you do stupid things...

It would certainly give you a moment of ass-puckering fear as you wondered if it was going to outright explode, but it didn't. It constantly threatened to, and it scared the shit out of me, but it never did actually explode. It was like a backfire or something.

The machine was too unpredictable and temperamental for me to mess with or try to fix. I was terrified that if I changed anything I'd never get it to light again. So, I lived with it, *all winter*. I even got to the point after a few days where I could sleep through it - you'd be amazed what you can get used to.

My "bed" at the time was a section of pallet racking, the same stuff you find in a warehouse. The unit was 10-feet long and by setting a shelf at about chest high, with a few 2x4's strung across and covered with a 4 x 8 sheet of plywood I had a serviceable bed frame. There was another shelf much farther up (perhaps 10 feet or so) and the end result was a massive 4-poster bed with an industrial groove. An old wrestling mat served as my mattress, and all in all, it was surprisingly comfortable.

The heater had been set up about six feet from my bed, I

moved it to as close as I dared, exactly on the line of fear between freezing to death and burning alive. I knew the fireball would stay low to the floor, and my bed was high enough to be safe, so I just lived with it.

A few days later, I was cuddled up with my girlfriend who had just come over to hang out a bit when it decided to do its little explodey-fireball cycle for the first time in her presence. I was well used to it by now but hadn't thought to warn her. When that thing shot off, she levitated fully three feet off my bed and screamed for Jesus.

A week later, it didn't even cause a pause in conversation.

I cursed that cantankerous death machine a thousand times but was unendingly thankful for the generosity of my old friend who kept me alive through that winter.

Thank you, Kent, you're still one of my personal heroes.

Stay cozy, friends.

13

THE YOYO AND THE FIRE
EXTINGUISHER

My passions are made manifest through the creative
application of power tools.

The older I get, the more appreciation I have for the
empowerment of owning quality tools. Certainly, there are
team and tribe allegiances that border on holy wars, but
I'm a complete tool slut and have my DeWalt's hanging on
the wall side by side with my Milwaukee's. I believe in the
right tool for the job: Klein's for electrical, Husky's for
greasy, Park for bikes, and Bosch for wood. I do my
engineering in Windows, edit video on a Mac, and use
Linux for hacking and computer projects. Each tool has its
strengths, and fanatics following blindly just end up
walking into walls.

For twenty-five years, I made a career of amassing as many
tools as possible and sharing them with every single person
I could. It's a hell of a way to make a living, but you get to
learn a thing or two in the process. I've seen fire-breathing
dust collectors, a grandmother shatter her dentures (while
she was wearing them!) with a kickback, and know the gut-
wrenching feeling of the SawStop gunfire when it brings
ominous silence to a busy workshop. I've seen a thousand
CAD students draw parts that can't actually be made, seen

well-intentioned people fuck up enough perfectly good tools and materials to fill a Home Depot, and watched a CNC guru fling a solid rooster-tail of blue chips like a firehose, thirty-feet across the room.

All of this has taught me that there are three golden qualities that all tools should strive to be: Intuitive, Invisible, and Internal.

A great tool should be intuitive. It takes a decade to master the use of a hammer. It doesn't matter if you're a framing carpenter or peening fenders in a body shop, it's going to take ten years of daily use for the average person to truly master that craft. If you're blacksmithing, tack on an additional decade, because that's not just a job - it's an art form.

But if you set a five-year-old next to a tree stump with a box of nails and a clawhammer, they'll figure out the basics in the first ten minutes. It's intuitive and fun because the form and function of the tool enhance its useability. While this certainly won't work for every single tool, the ones I reach for 80% of the time in my shop are highly intuitive. It may take weeks, or even years of daily use to completely master a tool, but the average person should be able to do basic functions on a tool with ten minutes of instruction at most. Typically, half of that is covering safety so that they don't immediately hurt themselves or damage the tool.

When I say invisibility is a commanding feature, I don't mean that you can't see it. What I mean by invisibility is that you don't have to be actively conscious of the tool itself, only its function and ability. You want the tool to get out of the way so you can focus on the task at hand.

A great example of this is the M12 Jigsaw by Milwaukee. Quite simply, it sucks. Certainly, it's a reasonably priced, capable, little tool that will get the job done when you need it. But to sell it at that price point, Milwaukee dropped a fair set of features that are only found in much more expensive saws. Compared to my Bosch jigsaw, which cost nearly double the price, it's a night and day difference. When using my M12, I have to constantly get my face right down to the work and blow the swarf off the guideline to make sure I'm still on track. With the Bosch however, using nothing more advanced than a little hole in a piece of plastic, exhausts air down onto the cutting area and makes it so that I can easily see my line throughout the entire cut without even thinking about it.

Both saws have plastic housing with vent holes in them. Both saws have an integrated cooling fan. But the simple design change to allow it to exhaust down into the cutting area versus out the side makes all the difference in the world for me as the operator. When you're using a jigsaw, you want to be able to focus on following the line, getting a smooth cut, and making the part you need with as little effort as possible. This simple design change puts the Bosch World ahead of the Milwaukee World because it gets the tool out of the way.

While it's important to "let the machine do the work". It's also important to get the damn machine out of your way so you accomplish the job.

A great tool is one that you don't have to be conscious of using, it simply becomes an extension of your body and an enhancement to your ability. This makes it invisible because you're not seeing or thinking about it, you're focused on your work.

The greatest tools of all though, the ones you will use and appreciate the most, are internal. You carry them in the six-inch toolbox between your ears that you'll spend a lifetime filling. These tools range from the ability to understand feeds and speeds, to recognizing G-Code, to building good habits like remembering to remove the tape measure from the wood before pulling the trigger on the chop saw (not that I've ever done that...). These lifelong skills will become invaluable, but like patience and discipline, knowing when to walk away for the day because you've fun out of fucks to give, and the ability to improvise, adapt, and overcome won't simply come to you overnight. Just like learning to use a hammer, these are skills that need to be honed, used, and developed over time.

At the end of the day, the measure of any craftsman is their ability to do what they can, where they are, with what they have. Filling your internal toolbox with a comprehensive set of useful skills is the single most important investment you'll ever make. What will make you stand out as exceptional isn't just learning the basics for the field you focus on but learning useful things in other areas as well. Your mental toolbox is the one thing that you'll always have with you, the thing that no one can take away from you. Feed your brain.

Let me give you an example.

In a time long ago and in a town far away, part of my job was to give science demonstrations to large groups of school kids. They would show up to the facility on a field trip and over the course of an hour I would do everything from enveloping them in an indoor snowstorm, to launching a metal ring a hundred feet high with an electromagnet, to making explosions, and even blasting lightning twenty feet in open air across the room.

It was a hell of a good time. They got to be entertained and we even managed to learn a thing or two along the way. When you're hurling lightning bolts and making explosions, it's not exactly a difficult job to maintain the rapt attention of people, even twelve-year-olds.

I'd done the demonstration a thousand times and was fully prepared when the three busses pulled up next to the lab and kids started pouring out and mobbing our front lobby. We gave them the basic safety briefing about how they were about to enter a room filled with things that will kill you the moment you don't respect them. Then we led the whole group into the main demonstration hall where I would do the show.

Now, this was a large industrial space. A room big enough that you could have fit several typical two-story houses in it side-by-side. The room was supported by I-beam columns spaced every twenty feet; at the base of every-other column around the perimeter of the demonstration area sat a standard fire extinguisher. Nothing special, just a basic extinguisher, the entire facility was full of them because of the nature of the things we played with and our well-justified predilection for safety. In twenty-five years, I never set a single student on fire, despite several classes where it really did seem like a tempting idea.

You've met those kids. I was one of them.

I was just hitting my stride, we'd launched the ring, learned about standing waves with the flame-throwing Ruben's Tube, and things were rocking along just fine when a plume erupted from the back of the audience, and everyone started coughing and yelling.

Someone's wee precious child had thought it would be a great time to break the safety seal on one of the extinguishers, pull the pin, and give the handle a squeeze. They only did it for perhaps a second, but in doing so they had just forced us to not only crash the show, but we had to evacuate the entire audience as well.

So we marched everyone outside into the parking lot while we tried to air out the demonstration hall. This left us in a shit situation where now the show was ruined, but all the kids, parental chaperones, and teachers were stuck in the parking lot because the busses wouldn't be back for another forty-five minutes.

How do you fix this? What would you do? These moments will sneak up on you as you go through life. You will face a moment when the world falls to shit and all the plans fail. Airplane pilots spend years in training and get paid serious piles of money, yet spend most of their time sitting on their asses and flirting with the flight attendants while things go on, perfectly fine.

The reason that pilots are paid so well is because they retain and re-train these skills for the rare moments that things don't go according to plan. Because of this, they can be calm and calculating in times of crisis. Even those flight attendants that you may think of as nothing more than a waitress with wings are actually highly trained professionals that can empty that lounge on wings in a matter of seconds if necessary and save hundreds of lives in the process.

Anyone can be a hero when things go according to plan, it's having the skills to fix the situation when shit goes sideways that will make you dependable and desirable.

I put on my jacket, grabbed a yoyo, and walked outside with the students.

For forty-five minutes, with nothing more than a yoyo, I was able to keep everyone calm, happy, and entertained while still giving a science demonstration. We talked about inertia, friction, centripetal force, momentum, tensile strength, biomechanics, and even the circulatory system and repetitive stress injuries.

It turns out you can learn a lot from a yoyo.

With nothing more than a kid's toy I was able to salvage the show and save the field trip. In the coming week, I got letters and cards from the classrooms, teachers, and parents expressing their amazement and apologizing for the crisis-causing kid. The whole event was a pivotal moment in establishing our reputation as a great place for a field trip, not because of all of the amazing demonstrations, but because of one weirdo with a yoyo.

The only reason I was able to do that was because I'd worked to fill my mental toolbox. I'd developed the mentality of "Improvise, Adapt, and Overcome," and I'd spent a little time learning the basics of how to use a yoyo. I didn't learn any advanced tricks, but just knowing the basics was enough to intelligently speak about how it worked and explain the science behind it. If you carry a lot in your mental toolbox, you can get by with very little in your hands.

Keep this in mind the next time you're strolling through the tool section of your local big-box store. You can spend a lifetime's wages filling a workshop with power tools, but make sure to spend some time as well as dollars. Explore, read, study, and see just how much you can pack between your ears.

There's so much to learn, and you're capable of such remarkable things.

Be the person that saves someone's day when things go sideways.

14

THE PARABLE OF THE FIRE PIT

In my backyard, there's a fire pit. One of those suburban campfire arrangements made from a few courses of small landscaping bricks set around a metal ring. It's about a foot deep, and it's the kind of thing that rational people just use as an outdoor focal point for people to sit around and have adult conversations about their kids, their maladies, and the jobs they hate.

By design, it's the kind of thing that you normally toss a few logs in, and it burns for a couple of hours. At the end of the summer, you shovel out the ashes and that's the typical life of a typical little burn pit in suburbia.

This summer, with considerable help from a dear friend and heavy equipment, I cleared about three thousand square feet of sumac that had overgrown a hill in the back yard, about eight feet high. The plants had been growing there for easily forty years and we piled all of them at the base of the hill. The mass of tangled bushes, festooned with the invasive choking grapevines left a pile roughly the size of a semi-truck trailer.

I let it sit for a couple of weeks to dry out a little and give it time for all the leaves to fall off, and then I set to work. Most of it was fluff, small bushy branches less than a finger's width. In the entire pile there wasn't anything more than perhaps five inches thick. A tangled mess of vines, with the occasional thornapple tree just to keep you in your toes. A pair of long-handled loppers took the majority of the pile and a small electric chainsaw for the little bit of big stuff.

Piece by piece, it would get cut to individual bits just short enough to fit in the wheelbarrow. When it was full, I would push it across the yard to the burn pit. The pit just happens to be perfectly sized to match the wheelbarrow, taking one load at a time. It takes about ten minutes to burn down, and about ten minutes to fill the wheelbarrow.

Now, I can't just burn the entire pile at once. It would save a huge amount of work, but it would also set the garage on fire, get me in trouble for violating half a dozen local ordinances, and certainly piss off the entire neighborhood.

I couldn't just toss it in a dumpster, that would have cost hundreds of dollars and required another round of heavy equipment. If I was in a hurry, perhaps, but I had the luxury of time.

But in tiny batches, I can nibble away at it one piece at a time.

It took the entire summer, at a leisurely but persistent pace. Some days I'd only do one or two loads, most days it would be a dozen or so. Sometimes I'd get the whole house together and we'd do fifty loads in an afternoon. Step by step, piece by piece, we processed and disposed of the entire gigantic brush pile.

This is an excellent lesson in building projects.

You've heard the old cliche that Time Equals Money, and

that's certainly true. But nobody ever stops and talks about the value of that statement's corollary. This is a concept that is a valuable thing to learn.

If you're patient and persistent, you can accomplish monumental, fantastic things on a negligible budget.

Project Thumper - a 144-million-watt impulse generator - took me fifteen years to build. But it only cost a few thousand dollars to do it. Pricetags to buy machines like that already built are typically in the range of a small house.

Stop being daunted by the cost of things, or the size of things. Everyone tells you to "dream big". I'm telling you to *build big*. Because the cost of things isn't a realistic excuse, not if you have the luxury of time. Stop being in such a big damn hurry and learn to embrace the process, the learning, the discovery.

It's not enough to enjoy the finished project. The process of exploration and creation, the thousands of things you'll learn through building it, that's the real payoff.

You'll fail sometimes. But the patient and persistent approach turns those failures into lessons and victories. Some of my greatest projects have been born of epic failures that delivered unexpected paths to ideas and designs I'd have never discovered otherwise.

Money isn't even real. Don't let the lack of funding, or just the perfect tool, or any other stupid foolishness kill your idea before it even begins. Take a shot, noes are free, and curiosity never killed anything but boredom. Make something, make it as big as you dare to dream, and share it with as many people as you can.

Piece by piece, step by step, simple tools and limited

resources can be leveraged to move mountains.

And this is the lesson of the fire pit.

.

15

VASECTOMY

The Children are our future; unless we come together and act now to stop them.

With all the talk about abortion lately, I haven't seen anyone talking about the obvious other side of the equation.

Biology is sexist as hell, and we as a society tend to ignore that fact. When it comes to love and reproduction, women are complicated, nearly mythical creatures of biochemistry, engineering, transport, and housing. Men, on the other hand, are regenerative syringes with bad thermal management.

The greatest argument against Intelligent Design is a fundamental understanding of human reproduction. Greater authors than I have written volumes on "The Miracle of Childbirth" and to me, the real miracle is that anyone would ever want to actually do that after seeing it even once.

People are icky.

Thankfully, we have a choice. Overwhelmingly though in our society, the responsibility is placed on women to control unwanted reproduction. This is especially true when it comes to more permanent solutions like tubal occlusion and such. For the most part, 99% of men go through their whole lives instantly ready to procreate regardless of their desire or cause to do so. For women, it's totally normal to bundle in sterilization as a follow-up to childbirth. It's the "you want fries with that?" of the OB/GYN world.

Think about it, how many women do you know that have their tubes tied? How many men do you know that have had a vasectomy? The difference in that ratio is overwhelming, stupid, and unfair.

For a woman to get sterilized requires a much more involved, invasive, dangerous, expensive, and complicated procedure than for a man. So why aren't we, as men, stepping up and taking responsibility for our own bodies? Why aren't we taking personal responsibility for our own futures?

Well, it's two main reasons really. The first is because we're dumb and most of you have never really thought about it. Most men have never taken the time to explore these options. The second is because OMG YOU WANT TO DO WHAT TO MY BALLS!? That's just you being a wus because you don't understand what actually happens. So, let's stop being both stupid and afraid of something we don't understand because such is not the behavior of a gentleman.

Thankfully for you, I happen to have a considerable amount of experience when it comes to what's exactly involved in a vasectomy. Because I've had one myself.

Back in 2003, I was finally able to get a vasectomy, and here are the facts you need to know.

It cost me $325.00 and that was without having any kind of insurance. $300 for the procedure, and $25 for the Tylenol prescription they gave me. I never had to take even one of them and threw the bottle away after it sat unused in my medicine cabinet for half a year.

It took 7 minutes, 4 seconds, and aside from the one little injection to numb the area, was completely painless. I've suffered worse injuries from an unremarkable morning shave.

It took a weekend to heal, and I was back to work on Monday with no problems. I personally never had any bruising or swelling.

Within two weeks I was able to have normal sex again.

Within a month I was completely back to normal in every way, and without the use of a microscope even I couldn't tell the difference.

Those are the facts, here is the story and the instructions for how YOU can take responsibility for your own life and jump out of the gene pool.

I contacted Dr. Kurt Helgerson in Kalamazoo (where I was living at the time) and it turns out I got exceptionally lucky. There are several ways to perform a vasectomy, but he had studied the "non-surgical vasectomy" which at the time was relatively rare in the US. It's very popular in Asia and had been in use for years at the time (even more so now). A regular vasectomy is a pretty non-invasive very simple procedure to begin with. This was even better; you don't even need a single stitch.

128

I will admit that the first time someone said "non-surgical vasectomy" the image that came to my mind involved a concrete block and a ball-peen hammer, but thankfully that's not how this worked at all.

I scheduled the appointment a couple of weeks out and the first thing he did was talk to me for fifteen minutes trying to talk me out of it. A vasectomy isn't readily reversible, this is a serious decision and commitment. While it is possible in most cases to reverse one, it's worlds more complicated and expensive to undo. You're talking about microsurgery here, it's a job. So, you have to be absolutely certain that you're serious about it.

Given that I had known I'd wanted this since I was about 12 years old, that wasn't a problem at all. He also instructed me to bring a pair of super close-fitting underwear. Think man-panties. You won't want boxers or even your nice loose briefs. You want to look like you're smuggling plums. Firm support is key, and you really don't want anything rattling around. The boys will have plenty of time to breathe later. For this adventure, you're going to want to strap in.

I arrived on a Friday afternoon. Kurt schedules all of his vasectomies on Friday so that you have the weekend off work to heal. The first few days after are critical, so you want to make sure you don't have to work or anything. You're going to have a very chill, boring weekend. Plan on it.
I walked in, signed in at the desk, and my seat hadn't even gotten warm before I was invited in to get to meet Kurt and get my butt up on the table.

I was more than a little nervous. Some guy is about to go rooting around in my sack, this isn't a normal thing for me.

Kurt was totally cool though and we talked. He asked me again if I was absolutely certain, and we began.

The show begins with dropping your pants and shedding any manner of pride, you won't be needing either for the next ten minutes. Since we're focusing on just the balls, and they're tucked in behind what is usually the main attraction, Kurt just tossed that over my shoulder and taped it in place to establish a clear workspace. He grabbed a disposable razor and gingerly shaved about a 1-inch square front and center on my sack.

Now, this is usually the part where a normal guy would get very interested in the ceiling tiles or whatever is happening outside the window. I, however, am a nerd and was raised by parents who worked in emergency medicine. Besides, how often do you get to see inside your own ball sack? I had to watch.

The one and only bad part was about to begin. Kurt pulled out a needle roughly the size of a baseball bat. It was a Victorian era weapon, with an ornate brass handle, a stainless plunger, and a glistening crystal syringe. I don't know what the viscous neon-green substance was that filled it, but it sputtered and fizzed when drops of it hit the countertop and floor.

At least, that's how it felt when he pulled out the little plastic syringe while working inches from my balls. Thankfully, he didn't stick it anywhere near where I thought he was going to. Because as far as I knew, this show was all about the balls. It turns out, that for pain, you just have to run interference between the balls and the brain. I explained to the good Doctor that there had been a wide disconnect between my balls and my brain since high school. Despite my objections, he insisted I get the shot.

You know that crease where your leg meets your pelvis? It's about there. And Kurt is a guy who knows how to rock out in a hip joint. I've had a lot of shots in my life, this one ranks between getting a shot in the arm, and getting a shot at the dentist. It's certainly not something I'd like to do for fun, but it's not that big a deal.

And that was the only painful or unpleasant part of the whole show. It's also the end of the foreplay. Up to this point things were very relaxed, very chill. We chatted and waited a few moments for the anesthesia to kick in. Understand, this is just a local (it numbs a specific, small area) not a General (knocks you out) anesthesia. I was fully conscious and aware through the whole thing. I could watch if I wanted to, I just couldn't feel anything he was doing.

His hands were moving with the skill and practice of a coin magician who had done a trick ten thousand times over decades. The next tool was always ready right where he needed it, and there were no wasted movements. I enjoy watching a skilled worker do anything from laying brick to carving marble, and Kurt was no exception.

Using what looked like a pair of 90-degree bent hemostats (that's a roach clip for you stoners) he started. This pair wasn't like a normal set though, the ends were sharpened down to points. With a flick of the wrist and in one smooth motion he inserted the points into the front of my sack and spread them open to make a very tiny hole. Scrotum skin is super stretchy, so instead of cutting a slit with a scalpel, he just made a little puncture and spread it open.

This is an incredible innovation. Because a puncture wound is a lot less damaging to the tissue than a laceration.

Because he didn't cut open a bunch of blood vessels, there's less to heal and almost no bleeding at all. This guy just opened a hole in my sack, and there are only a couple of small drops of blood. I've bled more from my sack just from losing a bet and having to shave it.

He reached in with what I am sure is some manner of highly specialized and expensive surgical tool, but I will never think of it as anything more than a crochet hook, and delicately pulled out a little tube. I was looking at one of my Vas Deferens! How cool is that! In seconds he secured it in two places, clipped in between, folded them over, and installed a couple of little stainless clips on each end. Then he gently put them back into the hole.

I now had STAINLESS STEEL IN MY BALL SACK. How badass is that!

He grabbed his surgical crochet hook and fished out the other vas, and in a few seconds had cut and clipped the 2 ends of that one and put them back in the hole.

Then he removed the little needle-pliers and the hole just magically closed right back up. He put a band aid and a cotton ball on the hole, the same as you'd get when you get your blood drawn. He un-taped the anaconda from my back (which is good, as my shoulder was starting to get sore) and put everything back in place. I packed everything firmly into my manpanties and stood up.

Exactly seven minutes and four seconds had elapsed since we began. I was impressed.

Five minutes later after settling up at the counter and getting my prescription I was in the car and driving myself home.

These guys are German levels of efficiency. Yet at no time was I hurried along or made to feel like a number, something that you get used to pretty fast in most medical situations. Kurt and his team were incredibly patient and understanding. I'm guessing they're used to a lot of nervous guys who talk too much when they're scared.

Not that I would do that... I'm a rugged man of the sea... wearing manpanties with a band aid on my balls.

I drove home and now is where the real self-responsibility begins. This is important, so pay close attention. Because this is where you get to choose if you want this to be easy and painless, or if you want to suffer for a couple of weeks with a five-color bruise and a sack swollen up to the size of a basketball. Because if you don't listen to this, that's what it's going to feel like.

I went home, had a pee to make sure everything was working just fine and got on my back in bed. I had my laptop and a whole stack of models to build. Get some snacks and a bag of frozen peas.

Make sure the peas aren't frozen together in a block. It should feel like a light, cold, sandbag. Lay on your back, relax, and let your nuts chill with the peas. If they ache, use the peas. If the cold gets uncomfortable, remove the peas. This cycle will go from one side to the other for the remainder of the day. For me personally, I didn't really use the peas that much at all. Your mileage may vary.

The big giant rule here is simple. STAY PUT! Until Monday Morning you don't get out of bed unless it's to shower or relieve yourself. You stay on your ass and don't move. It will be boring but get some models or read a book or whatever you have to do to stay very still right there in bed until Monday morning.

Here's why. The good Doctor worked very hard to learn a whole technique to give you a vasectomy with the bare minimum of cutting or breaking blood vessels. As a part of this, he installed some awesome new stainless-steel upgrades into your sack. Now your body is pretty smart, and over the next couple of days, it's going to build on to your upgrades and cover those little stainless clips in a nice soft protective layer of scar tissue. But that takes time! Your body needs a couple of days to get things all situated and safe for normal operation.

And it can't DO that if you're all up and about trying to do things. If you decide to go to work or play rugby or something, it's going to get all your danglybits moving around and those little clips will start snagging on and shredding all the tiny little blood vessels in your nutsack. This makes all kinds of little things bleed. It won't kill you, but I assure you that the resulting swelling, bruising, and pain will absolutely command your attention for the next several weeks.

I, being profoundly allergic to pain and suffering (it's why I wanted to avoid having kids in the first place), followed my doctor's instructions when he said to embrace the boredom and stay off my feet for the whole weekend. As a result of that, I didn't even need any of the Tylenol they gave me. It was completely fine and had a nice, boring weekend of reading and putting models together.

It was somewhere between the 1-2 week timeframe of after before I had any manner of desire to get laid. They don't really have to tell you, "don't have sex for a week or two", you're not going to want to. One of the fundamental rules of being male is "you don't mess with the balls". And given the warnings about keeping chill while they heal...

you're a monk for a couple of weeks just to be REALLY sure.

You're not instantly sterile. It takes about 25 orgasms or so just to flush out the entire system. So, at this point, even though you've had a vasectomy, you're still playing with live ammo and that's important to remember.

Now that you're healed and ready for action, the next thing to do is to have 25 orgasms (most people do this over a couple of months) and then report to the Dr to get a semen sample tested. Once you get that finished, they will give you the official all-clear, and then you're a member of the Tropicana Club.

All juice, no seeds.

I may have considered that "25 orgasms" a bit of a challenge, and it's a quota, not a timeline. So... call a few friends and see what you're capable of. Enjoy yourself. Just remember, you still have to use protection.

It's been fifteen years for me now since my vasectomy. And this is the state of affairs now.

I have never, once, had a moment of regret about getting it done.

Sex is exactly the same. Unless they have a microscope, nobody will ever be able to tell the difference. Ejaculation is still exactly the same volume, color, consistency, everything.

And while a vasectomy is not a substitution for protection from disease, I never, ever have to worry about getting someone pregnant.

And that is awesome. :)

Because of science and a skilled Doctor, I have the ability to choose to not have a kid. I get to choose to have a career and work a hundred-hour-weeks doing what I love. Because I would rather be an inspiration and education to a hundred thousand kids and make a dent in the world than be a really awesome dad to just one or two. I know that I cannot do both, and I'm thankful I get to choose.

Having children profoundly changes your life. There's nothing wrong with that. But I like my life. I like my job. And I have no desire to give that up and dedicate my entire existence to raising a kid. If I ever get a desire to be responsible for the personal care and raising of a young life, I'll get a puppy.
And I strongly suggest that if you are considering having a kid, no matter what stage in life you are at, that you go out first and adopt a puppy from your local shelter. Spend a year raising a puppy. Then compare all of that to what you would endure for a baby.

And then call Kurt, tell him I said Hi and that I'm still thankful and have no regrets. He didn't pay me to say any of this, I haven't spoken to him in many years. But he changed my life, and I will never forget his work.

Thanks, Doc.

EPICARICACY

ABOUT THE AUTHOR

Chris Boden, originally from Coopersville, MI, is best known as a science educator, entertainer, and engineer. Chris began writing books in 2019 with radiant success. When he is not penning prose of painful wisdom and irreverent humor, Chris is an engineer and professional YouTuber with four successful channels including Chaotic Good, Physicsduck, Chris Boden Live, and Atmosfär. In his spare time, he builds boats, plays with model aircraft, and enjoys a good game of chess.

Check out Chris's other books: *Surviving Life With Your Gigantic Penis* (2019) and *Soapbox* (2021) available on his website **www.captainboden.com** or on Amazon.

If you like what you've read and want to support and Chris as an up-and-coming author, you can also find him on Patreon – **www.patreon.com/chrisboden**

EPICARICACY

Made in the USA
Monee, IL
17 September 2022

13221714R00085